MULTIPLY HANDIC

HUMAN HORIZONS SERIES

MULTIPLY HANDICAPPED CHILDREN

by

Rosalind Wyman

A CONDOR BOOK
SOUVENIR PRESS (E & A) LTD

First published 1986 by Souvenir Press (Educational & Academic) Ltd,
43 Great Russell Street, London WC1B 3PA
and simultaneously in Canada

ISBN 0 285 650262 casebound
ISBN 0 285 650254 paperback

Photoset in Great Britain by
Rowland Phototypesetting Ltd,
Bury St Edmunds, Suffolk

Printed and bound in Great Britain by
Biddles Ltd, Guildford and King's Lynn

Acknowledgements

This book represents the efforts of a great many people, especially the parents of deaf-blind or multiply handicapped children whom I have met during my teaching career. I am particularly happy to acknowledge the help given to me by two parents, Norman Brown and Christine Taylor, whose thoughts are quoted extensively in the first chapter. I am indebted to colleagues of SENSE (The National Deaf-Blind and Rubella Association) who have allowed me to quote from articles which first appeared in *Talking Sense*: Judith Peters for her article on Motor Skills and Doreen Norris for her article on Starting Visual Training with the Deaf-Blind Child. I would like to express my appreciation to Paul Ennals, David Brown, Christine Dunn and Sally Silverman for their ideas, suggestions, outlines of play activities and for 'Rana's Day'.

I am grateful to the University of Texas at Dallas, Callier Center for Communication Disorders, for permission to quote from the Callier Azusa Scale; to the State of Michigan, Department of Education for permission to quote from the *Manual for the Assessment of a Deaf-Blind Multiply Handicapped Child*; and to Robert J. Smithdas for his permission to quote from his poem *Shared Beauty*.

Sincere thanks are due to Phil Grey for all of the photographs, to Gail Prout for the line drawings reproduced in this book, to Margaret Gomm for invaluable secretarial help and to Rodney Clark, Director of SENSE, for his encouragement. Most of all my thanks go to Al.

Whilst much of the work described has taken place at SENSE's Family Centre in Ealing and with families known to the Family Advisory Service, I should make it clear that any opinions expressed are those of the author and are not necessarily those of colleagues either within or outside of SENSE.

RW

Contents

'A person is deaf-blind when he or she has a severe degree of combined visual and auditory impairment. Some deaf-blind people are totally deaf and blind, while others have residual hearing and residual vision. The severity of the combined visual and auditory impairments means that deaf-blind people cannot automatically utilise services for people with visual impairments or with hearing impairments.

'Thus deaf-blindness entails extreme difficulties with regard to education, training, working life, social life, cultural activities and information. For those who are born deaf-blind, or who acquire deaf-blindness at an early age, the situation is complicated by the fact that they may have additional problems affecting their personality or behaviour. Such complications further reduce their chances of exploiting any residual vision or hearing. Deaf-blindness must therefore be regarded as a separate disability which requires special methods of communication and special methods for coping with the functions of everyday life.'

Definition of deaf-blindness which has been adopted by the Nordic countries.

1   The Parents' View

The advent of a child who is handicapped inevitably alters the life pattern and expectations of his or her parents and forces them to adapt, throughout the pre-school, school and post-school years, to circumstances which they may never have envisaged. Their entire lives will be affected.

Traditionally, when two people marry, they are expected to live happily ever after. As most of us know, that does not often happen: they will have to go through a time of adjustment to living as partners and eventually to living as parents. Most people, however, have certain expectations about marriage which are in fact often fulfilled. Despite the soaring divorce rate, many couples live harmoniously as partners and bring up happy and well-adjusted children. But for some parents, unfortunately, all does not go smoothly. They have a child who is diagnosed as handicapped and, from that moment, the partners may be driven or forced apart by circumstances and feelings beyond their control. This is something so serious, so fundamental and so often overlooked that we need to consider it very carefully.

Parents may feel as though they are 'stretched on a rack' when they are told about their child's handicapping condition. All too often they receive the news under very difficult and traumatic circumstances, and many break under the strain. Even now, in far too many hospitals, only one of the parents is told, thus inflicting an intolerable burden of emotions on the one who has to relay, often alone, the details of the child's handicap to the other parent. At this stage a plethora of misinformation and misinterpretation about the condition almost invariably creeps in, and it may take many years for parents to become clearly informed and to reinterpret details that have first been heard under emotional stress.

Even when parents are told together about the child's condition, this may not happen in privacy, and they may be surrounded by more than a dozen 'well-intentioned' professionals who are strangers to them. In such cases they often feel unable to express their grief or anxiety, or to ask questions of the paediatrician whose task it is to give them details about their child. Deeply felt resentment and anger can result from the mis-handling they receive at this crucial time. Parents and professionals should, together, always protest to any establishment which they know is not handling this first 'information-giving' time in a dignified and sensitive way (it is our duty to point out their duty!). We all know stories about parents who have heard the news of their child's handicapping condition under undignified circumstances and can tell of their feelings of isolation, grief, confusion and hurt. But very few of us can relate instances of people who say that they were given the news, however hard to bear, in as delicate and careful and kindly a way as possible. Until such instances become the general rule, it is up to us to act on behalf of parents who sometimes dare not protest at the treatment they have received.

If a child is not diagnosed at birth, parents may worry, together or separately, about their child's development, may hide their anxiety from each other or may tell one 'side' of the family but not the other. I have heard of parents taking the child to a paediatrician and to the Diagnostic Assessment Unit without telling their partner, and have known several mothers who have attended development play sessions with their children without telling the father.

Norman and Christine both have multiply handicapped children. They live in different parts of the country and have completely different lifestyles, yet they share the same problems, uncertainties and joys. Norman's son is nineteen and Christine's five. Both boys are profoundly deaf, with very limited sight and a communication system which only just allows their parents to understand and interact with them.

Both children's parents live their lives with heightened awareness, with a knowledge which sometimes they wish they did
not have about the medical conditions affecting their children,
and with the realisation that, however much they love their
children, they wish they were different.

Norman writes
I am moved to write, not because I have solutions, but in
the hope that my slowly increasing understanding, mostly
a result of hindsight, will be of help. I merely bear witness
to one experience and you must modify it with yours. One
other qualification I would make. I cannot speak for every
handicapped family, but only for a family with a member
having little or no formal communication. I think this is
important. There are many handicapped people with
whom I have shared full and rich communication, cheer-
ing the heart. Many points of which I write come from the
daily experience of continual care and contact without the
blessing of exchanging views, information and general
chit-chat with the person cared for. I would not like
anyone, especially any handicapped people who read this,
to think that having a disability in the family automatically leads to the considerations I shall note. I write for the
families, such as mine, with a child who, for whatever
reason, is called a non-communicating child. I use 'non-
communicating' to cover those who cannot use words or
signs to convey or receive abstract thought. Here I paint a
picture bleaker than I hope you find it.

When I consider the life of the handicapped family, the
problem areas form under four main headings—time,
guilt, grief and stress.

The needs of parents vary as the child grows, partly
because the needs of the child change, but also because the
parents are growing as well, with strengths and wants that
alter. But one consistent pursuit of mine has always been
the pursuit of time—time to understand and adapt but
mainly time to recover and in which to capture moments
that are just my own.

When our child first arrives, time flees. We are launched into an immediate and wearying race to claw back space in which to do the right things so that no one in the family suffers.

There is a five-fold quest in the first five years: for knowledge, diagnosis, treatment, rights and placements.

We are desperate for knowledge. What is wrong with my child? Why does my child not do those things? Why does my child do these things? Where can I go for help? Who will understand?

The truth usually unrolls slowly. Few of us discover the full picture straight away. A revelation leads to suspicion, to confirmation, to another suspicion, and so on as our quest for knowledge becomes a quest for diagnosis as well, and we whirl our confused way through a series of shocks. As each truth is stated, and even as we pursue the next, we seek treatment for the first, and sometimes are led into cul-de-sacs as we take steps that later prove futile because the whole picture was still unknown.

Christine writes
The white coats went into a huddle. A sister came in and said she was going to take some blood after all; she said the problem might be rubella. This was the first time that word was said and I didn't know what it meant or why she had said it. I was given an appointment to go back in four weeks.

Sunday, 25th March, was Mother's Day that year. The event that happened that day changed me from a normal run of the mill person to a mother of a visually handicapped deaf (rubella) child.

We cannot expect parents to be partners together until we know that both of them have at least had the chance to be involved in the knowledge of their child's developmental capabilities and his or her possible limitations. Once we have established this and can see them through their first, perhaps essential period of 'mourning' and readjustment, we can begin to hope that they will be able to work together as partners.

This time of 'mourning' may take anything from a minute to a week, a month or even a year and sometimes, as we all know, it never takes place. However, happily for the child, most parents do manage to adjust and the child becomes a much loved and equal member of the family. This does not take place overnight. In most families in which it occurs we find that it is as a result of the parents becoming involved with their child, knowledgeable about his condition, interested in his education and realistic about his future.

As soon as possible after diagnosis, good intervention with sensitive planning should take place. The sooner this happens the better the family situation will be in that most parents, having adjusted to their situation, need to feel useful again. 'What can we do?' they ask. 'How can we help?' Very often nobody answers.

Norman

It is a period of immense confusion compounded by the fact that each thing we need to know is in the realm of a different specialist, and the multiple journeys start. Those agonising waits for the appointment for which we arrive on time, after the most enormous hassles, only to find a crowd of others waiting, who have all been given the same arrival time. Consequently, when the specialist is finally seen, our child is so distressed, and has so distressed us, that any coherent dialogue is impossible. All we want to do is escape, as does the child. No tests work, the right questions are not asked, anything said is only half remembered, and we come away with only one concrete outcome—another appointment, when usually a different person will see us and require briefing from scratch.

Not only is there the problem caused by the treks out, there is also the problem caused by the treks in—other people's treks to our homes—these becoming more frequent as we move from considering knowledge, diagnosis and treatment to encompassing rights and benefits, and begin the quest for placements. The Health Visitors, the peripatetic services, the Social Workers, the advisors, the checkers of claims, all beat a track to our door and, if our problems increase, so do the visitors. We welcome them all, for we need their help, but we are often pinned down and vulnerable within our once safe refuge, our own home, subject to invasion when it suits others. The very response to outside agencies can be draining, and the duplication of effort immense. I have spoken to one Social Worker who stepped in to become the buffer between a mother and these agencies, and found that she had a list of 28 people likely to call or needing contact. At only one a day and once a month, that would leave not even the weekends free.

And all this is happening when we ourselves need time, in particular that all-important time, the time to accept; the time to realise that our child is still a child, a child with special needs, for whom no miracle cures can be awaited: just herself, just himself, with potential to be explored, love to be given or awakened and a dignity and life to be safeguarded.

Christine

At first he wouldn't breathe, then he did and was cleaned up to be given to me. When I held him he was so cold, so skinny; then he opened his eyes. They were pale blue. To me his eyes were something like a horror film. He is blind—my baby will never see me! It's all so vivid even now. What do I do? I think of white canes and dark glasses. He is so cold and so thin. I cannot express how I feel; my mind, my feelings of shock will not let me speak. The midwife fusses around us. My husband keeps walking up and down, saying over and over again, 'He is so thin, so pale, like a skinned rabbit.'

I hold Paul, trying to get him warm. I wish he would stop looking at me with those staring eyes. The midwife phones for a doctor and he arrives half an hour later. He examines Paul and is very concerned about his heart and his breathing, yet says nothing about his eyes. Paul makes no sound at all. All I want to do is hold my baby, he is so cold, but he is wrapped in a blanket and put in his carry-cot. I just can't take in all that is happening. I start to feel numb, my mind will not accept what is happening to us—this numbness stays with me for the next few years, whenever something painful happens to Paul. If I had been left alone with him for just a little while, maybe I would have let go and cried for both of us, and it would have helped me later when I was told Paul's handicaps.

The doctor tells me, with a good line in bedside manners, that he is going to take Paul to the local Special Care Unit for further examinations. I cannot go with him, I'm told, because I've just given birth, and anyway Paul will be home in about a week's time. The doctor keeps going on about Paul's heart, but to me then, at that moment, it is his eyes that matter. I wish someone would explain to me about his eyes. They take Paul away to hospital: it's windy outside, the time is 4 p.m. I hope they take good care of him, and please, please, God, let me hold him soon.

Norman
It took me seven years to accept—and I am still caught out.

We also need time to accept a new perspective, a new way of life, and time to accept other people's attitudes and to learn how to cope with them.

Christine
Paul is in a plastic oblong open box—something I've never seen before; I always call it a coffin. He has a breathing pad under him which bleeps all the time. How that bleep frightened me when it stopped at different times. I do wish parents are told why they are used; we didn't find out until after it had stopped the second time. The fear of that pad is still with me now. A young student nurse stands beside Paul all the time, like a prison warder. I ask if I can hold him. 'No,' I am told, 'he is far too weak.' She then began to tube-feed him, without telling me what she is doing. The shock of seeing this happen—the only thing it brings to my mind is force feeding, and I have

never seen anything like that before. A sister comes in and tells us that the paediatrician will be seeing Paul tomorrow—no doctors have seen him yet. My arms ache to hold him; I touch his tiny blue hand, it is so cold. The student nurse says we must go now as parents are only allowed in at feeding times.

At home our other son starts to cry. 'You promised me my brother would be here when I came home, why isn't he, when can I see him?' How do we explain to a three-year-old child? We sit and hold him and try to explain.

When there is a service that offers practical assistance, all parents are then able to help their children. It must be emphasised, however, that the offer of advice and counselling requires delicate planning. If the intervention is not handled properly, the end result is disastrous for both child and parents.

Norman
We can forget how to relax. We can also forget how to fill our time—our own time. When the child starts attending school, the mother may suddenly realise that her dedicated concentration on him has emptied her life of all other contacts and activities, so that suddenly there is nothing and the buzzing mind has only itself to turn upon—a strange backlash that even the working husband cannot share, for he does not experience that gap. We must be sure that our handicapped child does not become the only thing in our lives. We drive ourselves hard, don't we? We drive ourselves to do our best for our child, and we can also drive ourselves to avoid the issue, to block out the pain and shout down the doubts, for the problems of the handicapped child do not release us from all other problems; they merely become deferred or avoided until they can be avoided no longer.

Christine
I pick up Paul, he looks different—drunk. His pale blue eyes stare at me even more. A doctor tells me that Paul has

been given a massive heart stimulant; if he lives until morning he will be sent to a London hospital, as they can do no more for him. My whole being wants to scream. No one said anything about dying, my baby won't die. They still don't know what is wrong—why? They are doctors, why don't they know? I can still see Paul now as he looked then, my memory won't let it fade. I think that is why I so desperately want to help parents. I know in an instant my baby is handicapped, the doctor doesn't give him much chance of survival. I lay Paul back in his plastic 'coffin' and run out of the hospital. If ever I needed to believe in God's existence I really did that night.

Norman
How much time and how many words are currently spent on personal relationships. An average day's reading or viewing will convince you that nothing else exists. Yet in the handicapped family there is no time for such distractions. We can often forget that we are ordinary people underneath, because we are not supposed to function as such. We are the pivot and focus of a myriad involvements, all child-centred. Perhaps it is all background to my next point—the potentially divisive effect of the handicapped child. It is true that the child can draw families together, marshalling the father's protective instinct with the mother's care in a concerted effort to move mountains—and the mountains can move. But underneath other forces are at work. If we are not careful, marriage becomes a serious business and the humour dies.

Christine
Every other day we went to hospital. My husband gave up work and signed on the dole.

Many parents are 'dictated' to by professionals—being given appointments, asked to visit a bewildering assortment of clinics and specialists—and they may feel that they play a very small part in the life of their handicapped child.

Norman

How hard it is to face up to the problems in a relationship and discuss them. How easy it is to mistake the problem or defer the discussion when your child is assumed by all the world to have the overriding call on your attention. How difficult it is, even when you are willing, to find sufficient time and energy to tackle the discussion. How easy to feel your own problem is not worthy of note and therefore, that neither are you. But, unattended, the problem will fester until it becomes paramount.

The progress can be subtle. Amid the turmoil and the weariness, the good times grow scarce. The needs of the child are such that on most occasions at least one parent must be on hand. Baby-sitters can be arranged for special occasions, but for many meetings and social events such cover cannot be found, especially as the child grows older. Thus, such occasions are often refused or attended by one parent only. Before long an insidious process begins. If one's only contact is when one is solo, a subconscious feeling can emerge that good times are associated with absence from one's partner, and one's partner is associated with stress and strain. Very destructive. To this is added the fact that most professionals work office hours, so their visits to the home are usually to see the mother only. However much she tries to convey or intends to convey what she has learnt, she remains the one most in the know and most able to build upon that knowledge and upon her longer contact with the child. This can lead to the father feeling the redundant partner, his sense of inadequacy compounded by the rejection he faces as his fumbling efforts are spurned by the child who has grown to accept instruction from the mother only. Withdrawing further, he turns his effort to the supportive role, becoming more the breadwinner who will see his family lacks for nothing material—something he *can* do—and unwittingly leaving more of the direct care to his wife. Even that is no way out.

Christine

Two therapists came in and one said to the other, 'Oh, look, he isn't as bad as we expected.' What they were expecting I don't really know; it put me on my guard straight away. The therapists showed me how to strengthen Paul's trunk and, hopefully, his weak muscles. Paul cried the whole time, every time. But as the weeks went by his muscles did become firmer, although he still held his head back all the time. I was told that Paul's neck muscles were very floppy and I must make him hold his head up all the time, even when he was asleep. It became a 'thing' I kept doing all the time, but it made no difference, his head stayed back.

One evening, after he had brought his feed back at me again after I had taken three quarters of an hour to give it to him, and with him still not responding to me, I shouted at him, 'Why are you like this? Look at me! You are supposed to be a human baby not a rag doll! I want you to live, to grow up and be someone.' Paul cried and for the first time ever let me cuddle him, and I felt him respond to me. He was five months old and at last he felt as if he was mine, all mine. I had felt, up until then, ever since he came home from hospital, that he was a stranger, we had never had the time to be together. I had never tickled him, heard him laugh, seen him look for me around the room—all the little things I had done with my other son when he was a few months old. I never fell in love with Paul, I was always too busy feeding him, exercising his body, giving him drugs, trying to interest him in toys, with no response; and always I was so tired. I cried the tears I would have cried if he had been allowed to stay at home with me in the beginning and not been taken away from me one hour after birth. From then on, although things were up and down, I slowly grew to love him as a baby and not the handicapped rag doll I was looking after automatically.

It is important to emphasise that we 'professionals' must see ourselves as partners in the parents' team and not the other way round. The parents know the child, have assessed his abilities and have observed him (often minutely) over a longer period of time than the professional. Parents also know in great detail the services they have already received, their efficiency and the need to build on them. They know their present situation very well, too—where they live, what toys they have, what equipment they would find useful, their abilities, how much time they have and so on. They also know the child. They know their hopes and plans for the future and invariably want the best for their child. We could say, therefore, that professional people should regard parents as their professional partners, working together to obtain the best possible service for the child and his family.

A goal planning method is a useful and constructive way of working; it can help all parents to be useful, constructive teachers. When the child succeeds, week by week, we should see that achievement as *his* success, stemming from the parents' effectiveness. If the child fails, for whatever reason, the professional involved should see the failure as his or her own failure in not setting the task carefully enough, not planning the goal realistically. Specialist teachers, therapists, etc., must realise that they are the parents' partners and they have a duty to pass on their skills, so that the child is stimulated in the home setting as well as in the specialised setting. Physiotherapy should not be confined to hospitals and special schools. We must alter situations where we hear parents say that children only get speech therapy once a month. Speech takes place all the time, bodies move all the time, children grow and learn all the time. Parents must feel able to contribute to their child's all-round developmental needs.

This sounds as though I am burdening the parent with a great deal of work or denying the role of the teacher and the therapist. This is not so. I am putting in a plea for the parents' abilities and saying that if we planned with the parents, and not separately from them, together we should achieve so much more.

Norman

One can give a great deal to a job if one has a secure base to return to. If conditions in that base are stressful and require continuing effort, both job and home suffer in the long run. The person at home cannot look for relief when the paid working partner returns, and indeed feels guilty at needing that relief instead of being able to provide it. The paid working partner comes home for a new shift rather than relaxation, and feels guilty at being unable to fulfil expectations. Both look for respite, even from one another, for the presence of the partner is a constant though unspoken cry for help, and weariness is mistaken for reluctance even by the weary.

Thus isolation closes in as the world, already small, contracts to what we can cope with, and we shrink away, even from one another, or tire of our own complaints, until we feel that in each other's eyes, and in our own, too, we have become some kind of monster.

The world turns over. Those times to which outsiders look forward—the great festivals and holidays—become the times we dread, for our periods of greatest stress are borne when everyone demands a show of happiness. So we pretend, and move a little further away.

Our dreams on ice, we feel our energies must turn to the child. We seek an appropriate programme and then seek to make it effective. Recognising the need for consistency, we make our home a school. For some time it does not matter; it is naturally done for any child. Labels and signs appear, the furniture changes, ornaments and books move further up the walls, toys are scattered everywhere. But for how long can you keep this up? If your home is a teaching environment, when does it become your home again, and when do you become just Mum and Dad?

I am not so naïve as to say, 'You must make time to be together and talk together and have fun together', for I know that often it really is impossible. Making time is easier spoken of than achieved, especially when you are living at so many people's mercy; but nonetheless, capture it when you can.

Christine
At about nine months, my Health Visitor agreed that Paul should have some help from a peripatetic teacher, as whatever I could do for him was not enough. I needed some help.

A teacher came on the scene. She was marvellous, a peripatetic teacher for handicapped children . . . She came once a month and we all so much looked forward to her visits. My other son would wait at the front gate and, when she drove up, would help her in. She always had a large laundry basket full of toys and used to chat away to my son, asking him how he got on at play group that day. Her theory was that if Paul could not get to the toys, then the toys would have to come to him. She introduced Paul to all kinds of 'feels', every texture; she had a book of carpet squares and would very gently encourage Paul to touch them. She showed us how we could make home-made toys rather than use plastic all the time; she told us about books we could read and even told me about the Attendance Allowance. How we loved that hour. At last someone was helping us to help Paul. The hour she stayed passed so quickly, and when she left she always left two toys for Paul and an 'unofficial' one for my other son. He used to help the teacher put all the toys back in her car, which was full of toys, and we waved goodbye, longing for the next time she called. Her guidance really started us on the road to helping Paul learn to play. She treated Paul as a child who needed help, never the medical 'rubella' child.

Parents should be seen as equals—equal co-workers with children, equal advisors and potentially as able as any other person of like ability. Professionals and parents have certain specialised and generalised skills which they can pass on to each other for their mutual benefit. Professional people need to

adapt and adjust just as much as we ask the parents to do.
Perhaps a true story will help to illustrate this. A child born to
Hindu parents was unable to tolerate milk and was slowly
starving to death. The dietician spoke to the Hindu mother
about the problem and, realising that she was very devout,
said, 'I know you are a Hindu but the only formula that I can
find to keep your child alive has beef extract in it.' The mother
replied, 'God has given me this child, so God will have to
readjust his thinking. Give her beef.' And the child thrived.
Like so many parents, this mother was able to adapt to meet
her changing circumstances. As professionals, we must remember that parents have had to make tremendous adjust-
ments, and we should not expect them to be convenient
stereotypes. We all have different hopes, different fears, different needs. We must recognise all these needs and all these
differences and, having done so, we should also see the advan-
tages of working together for our mutual benefit. It is only
when we are truly equal co-workers that the children we are all
serving will be treated, cared for and educated as effectively as
they deserve.

The parenting role may assume additional proportions
when a multiply handicapped child is present in a family. It is
invidious to think of all parents of handicapped children as
belonging to a group, although there are some factors which
place them in a unique group situation. Every parent is an
individual and deserves recognition of his or her personal
value.

Norman
I think of parents as ordinary rather than as specially
chosen, although I will allow that going through the fire
may refine us a little. We have our own talents, strengths
and weaknesses. Sometimes a parent who might otherwise have chosen to work with handicapped children has
such a child, and finds a rich fulfilment in the child's care
and education. Sometimes, as in my case, a parent's
talents seem all to lie in other fields and nothing seems to
come naturally, so that the child's rearing becomes a

learnt and arduous process. Sometimes the force of circumstances, together with personal and family composition, makes it impossible to manage—and the difference between survival and breakage can be only a hair's width. Yet the strength of love may be equally strong in all cases.

Thus we cannot judge one another. Love does not conquer all, it endures all.

Christine
I have always felt guilty that my body did this terrible thing to Paul.

It is clear that working with young multiply handicapped children and their families can often involve intense support and parental education, so that in these vital early years the parents will receive enough back-up and guidance to re-establish themselves in their own eyes as effective and worthwhile adults. Some parents will need to be helped to see that they have value and that within the family they can be effective educators of their own children.

Christine
I longed to meet other parents with children like Paul. I longed for my older son to have the opportunity to play with children who had a handicapped brother or sister, but I was told by everyone that Paul was the only rubella handicapped child in my town. I felt so alone. I felt that if Paul had had a handicap that was more commonly known we would have found a kindred spirit. We felt cut off from the world and so we cut ourselves off even further. We only mixed with people who would not stare if Paul held his head back or behaved in an unusual way. At times I used to smile to myself when under-fives threw temper tantrums in shops or in the street. I felt that nobody stared at those children but that everyone stared at us. I was no longer one of the crowd but always felt slightly out of step. Sometimes I longed to be like a sheep in a field. Anonymous. Ordinary again.

Norman

The decisions on the way are grievous and may cause divisions. They are another cause of stress and may even make us feel cut off from other parents who have followed a different road. If you have doubts you must learn to forgive yourself as you would forgive others in a similar plight. Some would say that between the handicapped child's needs and the parents' needs lie the brothers' and sisters' needs, putting back even further those of the parents, and providing fertile ground for further guilt and worry. How do the other children react? What effect will it have on them and their future? The question 'What are they missing?' becomes 'What am I depriving them of?' Can they take second place in my time and not feel they are taking second place in my love? Will they suffer through not having a normal life? What is normal? It is what I perceive as the standard, drawn from press, television and books, or the comments of friends. For a child, what is normal is what I am used to, and it is only when someone points out how abnormal I am that it touches me.

Christine

Paul has shown me a new meaning to life. The natural world now looks so different to me. The goals that took Paul so long to achieve, like sitting up, feeding himself, walking, I treasure more than mothers of normal children.

Norman

They take some hard knocks from us. We come to expect much from them and they back us. How many times do we struggle through the day until at last the handicapped child is at peace? And the second you breathe that sigh of relief, the brother or sister appears with a pain or a problem, silently saying, 'It's my turn now. Now make an effort with me', and you have no effort left. Suddenly your young ally becomes your young enemy and you snap back, seeing the hurt in his eyes and overwhelmed by the waves of your own misery and guilt. But children are not built by such moments. They are built by the others, when your arm is around them and the bedtime stories told, when the laughter rings out and silliness reigns, when the tears are shared and the interest shown and the tired parent, after the snap, gives that little extra special time that heals all. Such times do happen. It is hard to grow up in a situation in which you cannot compete, where, no matter how strong the case for attention you present, there is always another more pressing demand. It is harder still when you are in competition with someone you love.

Brothers and sisters have equal needs within the family.

Christine
If Paul goes anywhere we all go together. As a family we cope together. I have seen couples destroyed by the demands of the handicapped child. It is not going to happen to us.

Norman
I do not know whether it is easier to be the older or the younger brother or sister of a handicapped child. Does the period of undivided attention you received before the arrival of your young competitor give a stable base on which to build, or does it merely make the trauma worse when such a powerful rival appears? Does a younger brother or sister find it easier to accept the situation as it is found? It is pointless to speculate because we have to deal with situations as they are.

Christine
If the tension gets too bad we talk it out.

Norman
As they struggle to make sense of the world, they must also absorb the effect of a disabled brother or sister in that world. Earlier than most children, they will become aware of the fallibility and vulnerability of parents. Although striving for their parents' attention and time, they will also begin to share with their parents some of the hurt and pain which could lead to resentment of their brother or sister. Yet resentment is forbidden them. You can fight with your brother and let natural resentment escape that way. But not if he is disabled. All must be sublimated. Confusions may manifest themselves in an over-solicitous concern or in withdrawal. It is a lot to handle . . . They love their brother or sister and feel so helpless, indeed are often pushed away. They love us and do not like to see us so consumed. Their own needs are but part of the whole. Their outbursts are against us because there is no one else to be against. If you are supposed to love everybody, at whom do you scream about the injustice of it all?

Christine

We at last found a haven somewhere where we didn't have to explain about Paul. We met parents like ourselves for the first time. We now knew that we would be all right. We could get all the help we needed and could relax for the first time in five years. Now Paul has a chance. Now it is up to him. We think he will make it. The pale, cold rag doll who was so weak and tiny is capable of growing into a strong, communicating, intelligent human being. He has potential. He has life. He is willing to learn. He wants to be part of this world.

What parallels can we draw from Norman and Christine's stories? Most parents realise that they will have to make conscious, long-term decisions about the way they will bring up their children, the way they will be educated and their lifestyle. All of these choices are different for the parent of the multiply handicapped child, and indeed they may have no choice offered to them. They are faced with a bewildering number of facts which they are asked to absorb, they are told that their child is going to need the care of 'experts', so that their image of themselves as adults capable of bringing up children immediately shatters. They have to learn to work with professionals whom they had never imagined encountering. They become isolated because of their child's disability, and then search for other people with whom they can identify. The brothers or sisters of the handicapped child may need even more attention and love because they feel that they have lost importance in their parents' eyes. Many parents ride the storm and families do stay together, despite the enormous pressures which they are asked to cope with. And many do not survive. Only parents who, with full knowledge, adopt handicapped children, ever think of leading a life with a child who is other than non-handicapped.

We need to help parents of multiply handicapped children to regain a sense of worth and dignity. The way society views handicapped children can further burden their parents and can make them feel strangers in their own town. When Christine

The multiply handicapped child needs the support of parents, they in turn need the help of the community.

allowed us to care for her son Paul during the summer holiday she reported that, even though he was not with her when she strolled along the beach, she still felt handicapped. To such an extend did Paul's handicap seem to reflect on her, her husband and her other son. Our role as professionals who are working with parents of severely handicapped children is to give them the ability to restructure their thinking about their unique situation and, within this, to give them help and support whenever they need it. Everyone nowadays expounds the theory that no child should enter an institution and that he should receive care within his community. If that care is not provided, if we do not give parents the confidence that they have our positive support, then we shall, all of us, have failed. We cannot let this happen.

2 The Family Advisory Service

As the result of a survey carried out in 1983, SENSE (the National Deaf-Blind and Rubella Association) established a national advisory service for deaf-blind children and their families. This book will outline some ways of working with some of our children, who may have been described as multiply handicapped because they may have disabilities additional to their sight and hearing problems. Usually, but not always, the children's dual sensory impairment has been viewed by *other people* as secondary to their additional disabilities.

Prior to 1970, a great many multiply handicapped children were deemed to be ineducable and were cared for within the Health Service. A major change in provisions for handicapped children occurred as a result of the 1970 Education Act in which it was stated that all children, whatever the severity of their handicap, should be educated and should be the responsibility of the Department of Education and Science. This, at the time, was heralded as a breakthrough by the parents. At last their children were seen to deserve the same chance of education and treatment as others, warranting all the special facilities previously denied them. Unfortunately, although provisions for minority groups can be the subject of legislation, attitudes cannot be changed so easily. Today most children, whatever their handicapping condition, are seen as whole people by the providers of services, but it has to be said that sometimes, when meeting angry, disillusioned and frustrated parents who feel that they or their children have been labelled or compartmentalised, we have to wonder how long it will be before all our children are seen to be worthwhile and their parents to be valuable. Attitudes of parents to their children, of professionals to parents, of professionals to other professionals, of society to handicap, greatly influence what will happen to the child in his early years, what type of education will be provided for him and the sort of adult he will become.

Children referred to the Family Advisory Service will have a variety of handicapping conditions and may therefore be difficult to categorise in educational terms. Some may eventually go to schools for the hearing or visually impaired, deaf-blind units within other special schools, to schools for children with severe learning difficulties, or may be integrated into infant and junior schools. Very often the children's capabilities may be masked because it is difficult to diagnose with any certitude the real nature of their educational need, and they may be placed in special care units because there is no appropriate facility for them within their locality and their parents do not wish them to leave home and go to boarding schools. The educational placement of a deaf-blind child may often prove extremely difficult, and the assessment procedures which he undergoes to ensure that he is provided with the most suitable education to fit his needs may be even more taxing for parent, child and professional.

The Family Advisory Service exists to bring help to the families of, and professionals working with, young children who have a dual sensory impairment. The advisory teachers, each with his or her own area of responsibility, are based in Newcastle, Birmingham and London. The service is provided for families living anywhere in England, and a limited service is provided for those living in Wales, Northern Ireland and Scotland. The team of advisory teachers is supplemented by advisory people such as a paediatrician, a speech therapist and a physiotherapist.

Very often the children with whom we work are aged between two and five years, but we have an increasing number who are referred to us at only a few months old. These are the lucky children: they have already been recognised as having a dual sensory impairment, so that the right services and treatment can be offered to them as early as possible. When we meet older children who have not been diagnosed or recognised as having serious sensory impairment, we often find that they are under-functioning. This may govern the way a child learns throughout his life. The earlier the diagnosis is made, the earlier a structured programme of intervention can be offered by all of the services available. The child and the family will need all the help they can get. The parents will need to know not only about his handicapping conditions but how to ame- liorate these. They will probably need the advice of teachers for the hearing impaired and visually impaired, help from physiotherapists, occupational therapists and speech therap- ists, their Health Visitor, their general practitioner, consul- tants in genetics, paediatrics, audiology and ophthalmology, as well as social workers, psychologists and other involved professionals. Very often none of the people within this for- midable list has met a deaf-blind child before. Certainly it is very unlikely that the parents will ever have imagined that their child, or indeed any child, could be affected by two serious sensory handicaps.

Children are referred to the Family Advisory Service by professionals and parents seeking help and advice so that they can work more effectively with the child in their care. Young children who have a dual sensory impairment cannot auto- matically benefit from teaching or therapy designed solely for children with only one of those impairments. Such children have to be considered as probably having communication problems which may jeopardise their further understanding and learning unless tackled early. Realising the importance of early intervention, the Family Advisory Service team appreci- ates the earliest possible contact with the child and his family, so that it can offer teaching advice, guidance and support during the child's vital early learning years. The Family Advis- ory Service seeks to work in close co-operation and to mutual advantage with all those who have a professional responsi- bility towards the child and the family. In particular, the aim is to ensure that the parents of the young deaf-blind child should be knowledgeable, confident and secure in their understanding of the child's condition and of the best ways to help him achieve his full potential.

The service operates by providing a variety of activities in the child's home, at a Family Centre, school or nursery. By visiting the home the advisory teachers can help parents and other involved professionals to choose the most appropriate play and work activities. They are helped to monitor their child's progress and to increase their skills in the observation of his development, so that they are enabled to initiate further activities for themselves. Often the home is the ideal place to meet the child's other visiting teachers and therapists, thus establishing co-operative effort and avoiding duplication of services. Essentially, the home visiting service can help parents to provide a developmental programme which has been structured specifically for the individual child within his own natural learning environment.

Formal tests are usually inappropriate for the needs of very young handicapped children, so we use detailed and systematic observation methods of recording the behaviour which the child shows in his most familiar setting. Records of the child's physical skills, fine motor and manipulative abilities, visual and hearing skills, method of communication, cognitive abilities, social and self-help levels, his ability to play, imitate, follow instructions and manipulate the environment, can all be obtained at home. Appropriate play and relevant activities can thus be recommended.

Appropriate teaching tasks are suggested so that the teaching remains geared to the child's needs and his progress monitored carefully. This service is seen as extremely important from the parents' point of view, as many of the skills which are expected of young children are (or should be) controlled by the parents. Feeding, toileting, dressing, washing and most social skills are the province of all parents until such time as the child goes to school. Through the early intervention work we can often provide parents with useful ideas in helping the child to attain mobility, and can certainly assist them in trying to ensure that, as far as possible, he will be given appropriate age/stage-related activities in co-operation with the child's other involved professional worker.

We are often able to arrange for parents to bring their

children (handicapped and non-handicapped) to a Family Centre to stay for a few days. Parents are enabled to visit both within the working week and at the weekend, and are always invited to bring with them their other involved teacher or therapist, and we find that they are always delighted to attend. When parents come to us, they feel that it is a place for the whole family to learn together: it is a place for teaching sessions, a place for the interchange of information between parents and professionals, a resource centre, a place for information, a place for advice on welfare and statutory rights, a place for learning together and for mutual support.

When the children arrive, we ensure that the non-handicapped brother or sister will have a worker assigned to him or her for the whole period if this is thought to be advisable, so that unnecessary divisions between brothers and sisters can be avoided. We structure the time spent so that parents can feel that they and their children are in a family atmosphere, and time is allowed for everyone to discuss and plan their requirements. We include the non-handicapped brothers or sisters within this plan as far as possible, so that they feel that they have an importance and a worth within their family. We often find that the non-handicapped child has become emotionally scarred because of the time and attention which is being spent on the handicapped child. If this is the case, then we will try to help parents appreciate that all their children have a permanent need for their time and attention, and that the abilities of all their children are of value. Sometimes parents can be so absorbed in the 'programme planning' of their handicapped child's life that they have forgotten to praise their other children for progress and achievement.

Staff of the Family Service invariably send follow-up reports to parents and involved professionals, and are usually able to visit the child's home, nursery, school or other placement at the invitation of the professionals and parents concerned, to give further advice on the child's global needs.

The Family Advisory Service staff have become increasingly committed to organising workshops for parents and professionals in England. Sometimes these are completely structured courses; at others they include a social event and a parents' meeting. Crèche facilities can be provided, so that both parents can attend courses together if they wish. The workshops are designed to give people the opportunity of learning alongside others about the general needs of the young multiply handicapped or deaf-blind child. Reference is made to the parents' own particular needs throughout these workshops, and we arrange to have enough time for group discussion so that parents with similar problems can share their experiences. Many parents have allowed us to videotape their children so that we can use tapes to demonstrate some teaching techniques and vividly illustrate some vital points. The workshops aim to give theoretical as well as practical assistance in helping parents to evolve techniques for training their child's residual vision and hearing, helping them to acquire good communication skills, assistance in establishing mobility and in attaining self-help skills (feeding, dressing, toileting, washing).

All the parents whom we meet see the necessity for establishing early communication with their children. They understand, probably better than anyone else, that the primary need for any multiply handicapped child is to make relationships and communicate with people. Until the child learns to respond actively to the pleasures of communicating with other people, the parents may often be as frustrated as the child, for they cannot make sense or meaning of the world for their child. The child's first teachers are his parents, but if his parents are unable to feel that their child is interacting with them, then they may lose the incentive to play, thus starting the vicious circle where neither parent nor child has the incentive to interact with each other. It is for this reason that throughout the year we also organise 'communication courses', so that groups of parents of young children can learn together of the ways in which they can help their children to communicate effectively. We recommend for most of our children what is sometimes called 'total communication'. The importance of the need for communication cannot be emphasised enough and the subject will be discussed in greater detail in Chapter 7.

The physical needs of children are usually assessed by the

Family Service physiotherapist who can write detailed advice for parents concerning some important aspects of their child's motor development. She liaises with the child's own physiotherapist or occupational therapist and, through her experience with deaf-blind children, is able to offer them invaluable recommendations towards the child's programme. We are often asked to provide specialist reports for children for whom a Statement of Educational Needs is to be prepared by Local Education Authorities, and parents.

All our work and advice will be based on the individual needs of the child and the requirements of the family as a unit. Whether the child is seen at home by the visiting advisory teacher or at a Family Centre, will depend very largely on the parents' needs at the time of referral. The programme of intervention is based on the premise that we are seeking ways of providing the child with experiences which will help him to progress, in his own way, through those milestones necessary to his developing independence. Our work is designed to help everyone involved to become more effective in their work with the child. The aim is to stimulate and motivate the child to use all of his abilities in all areas of development, and to encourage him to function at his optimum level by learning to communicate. Children may acquire new skills rapidly or slowly, according to their abilities and to the environmental influences which impinge upon them. Parents may need help in understanding how to modify the environment or the activities in which they wish their child to participate, and they may always need some help in observing his developmental progress. Parents may need to observe a teacher or therapist working with their child before they are able to implement the advice suggested, or may wish the teacher or therapist to see them working at home on certain programmes. Demonstrations of the methods and techniques to be employed may be necessary, particularly when embarking on the teaching of any skill co-actively. (The *Co-active method* is described in greater detail on p. 132.)

Having helped the parents to structure the child's learning environment and encouraged them to think of themselves as

competent teachers of their children, we may still have to help
them to gain an appropriate frame of reference in which they
can see the child's development in a positive manner. It may be
necessary to help parents take a careful look at their child's
development both in detail and as a whole. This can sometimes
be achieved without the use of a formal assessment tool, but
we often find that in order to discover the areas in which the
child can function at his best and what conditions are limiting
him, we may need to use developmental guidelines such as
those in the Callier Azusa Scale which was designed by the
Callier Center for Communication Disorders at the University
of Texas at Dallas, to aid in the assessment of deaf-blind and
severely and profoundly handicapped children. The Scale has
the specific purpose of providing the assessment information
necessary to 'synthesise developmentally appropriate activi-

Parents and professionals are equal partners in the child's
team.

Feeding. Hand over hand, the adult guides the child to hold the drink and bring it to his mouth.

Washing. Hand over hand, the child is helped to learn to reach for the towel to dry himself.

Dressing. Hand over hand, the child is shown how to pull up his socks.

Toileting. Hand over hand, the child is shown how to pull down his pants.

Signing. Hand over hand, the child is shown how to say, 'Want play'.

Exploration of objects. Hand over hand, the child is shown how to manipulate her toy.

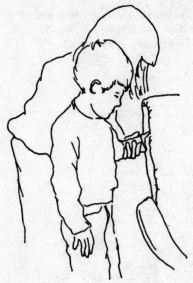

Exploration of the environment. Hand over hand, the child is shown how to trail his route from one place to another.

Visual training. Hand over hand, the child is shown how to reach for the torch that attracts him.

Auditory training. Hand over hand, the child is shown how to beat the drum that he hears.

Play activities. Hand over hand, the child is shown how to start the musical toy.

Swimming. Hand over hand, the child is shown the water before she steps in.

ties for a child and to evaluate a child's developmental progress'. It is composed of eighteen sub-scales in five areas:

Motor Development
Postural control
Locomotion
Fine motor
Visual motor

Daily Living Skills
Dressing and undressing
Personal hygiene
Feeding skills
Toileting

Social Development
Interactions with adults
Interactions with peers
Interactions with the
   environment

Perceptual Development
Visual development
Auditory development
Tactile development

Cognition, Communication and Language
Cognitive development
Receptive communication
Expressive communication
Development of speech

The main reason we use this scale is that it provides examples which

> describe behaviours observed among deaf-blind children functioning at that particular developmental level. Since the example behaviours take into account the specific sensory, motor, language, and social deficits of some deaf-blind and severely and profoundly impaired children, the behaviours sometimes differ from behaviours typically observed among normal children at the same developmental level. No specific testing expertise is required other than good observational skills and a knowledge of the child's repertoire of behaviours. Most accurate results are obtained if several individuals having close contact with the child (teachers, aides, parents, specialists) evaluate the child on a concensus basis.*

* Reprinted from the Callier Azusa Scale by permission of the University of Texas at Dallas, Callier Center for Communication Disorders.

Other assessment scales relevant to the needs of multiply handicapped children are listed in Chapter 7. (No observational scale that we use would attempt to measure intellectual ability; assessment of this type is not our province. All assessment procedures which we use are to help us observe in more detail the skills of the child, so as to formulate an effective programme of development for him.)

The assessment of any young deaf-blind or multiply handicapped child will be extremely difficult and will present many problems for the assessor. For example, when a visually handicapped child is suspected of having a hearing loss, the audiologist may have difficulty in adapting his approach so as to gain the maximum information from the hearing tests. A deaf child with a visual impairment may not fully understand the test situation and may be unable to co-operate, and where there is an additional physical or mental disability the problems for the tester are even greater. Some rubella-damaged children may have hearing and vision difficulties which may vary and often deteriorate, and in some deaf-blind children Eustachian tube blockage, sometimes referred to as 'glue-ear', may further compound their problems. Serious anomalies and differences in the treatment provided can often be caused because of the difficulties involved in the assessment of children having a dual sensory impairment. Assessments that take place in the child's most familiar environment and over a period of time will usually help involved professionals to design programmes and to provide placements that will meet the needs of the multiply handicapped individual.

The child's vision or lack of it will affect the rate at which he learns, will affect his ability to learn from his environment and will alter his perception to a lesser or marked degree. The child's hearing or lack of it will affect his response to people, and his understanding will be reduced or increased depending on his ability to interact with others. His ability to move will alter his perception of his environment to a considerable degree. If he has disturbed balance or uncontrolled muscles, limited reach or difficulty in interpreting sensory information; if he is unable to express himself freely, then he will need an even more careful and long-term assessment than those children without physical problems.

Once the child's difficulties in learning have been assessed and his condition diagnosed, it is important to make certain that provision has been made for an on-going assessment from all people concerned with him. Written information about the way his condition will affect his learning should be provided, together with his potential strengths and possible weaknesses and the area in which they are likely to be of greatest concern. Wherever possible, a detailed description of the child's vision, including specific details concerning its effect on learning, and of the child's hearing, together with an audiogram, should always be attached to any records that are kept, as a guide to those concerned in the child's development. This careful procedure and on-going assessment picture will help everyone to provide what the child needs when he needs it. The Family Advisory Service team would always, as a part of their work, try to help parents to collect this information for themselves and would encourage them to list their observations of the child's skills and behaviour at home.

What is assessment for? Are assessments produced for information about the child or are they to help all involved people towards positive action and good goal planning? The assessment team are of course concerned that action should be taken and no assessment will generally take place unless it is as the basis for further procedures. The assessment team may consist of parents, paediatricians, therapists, teachers, psychologists, health visitors and sometimes social workers and psychiatrists. They will use as their basis for the assessment the normal developmental sequences which all children are expected to attain. At present, all parents have the right to access on information about their child and assessment for schooling must include, by law, their involvement in the whole procedure. The normal developmental sequences should be seen as the usual pattern which most children will achieve, but it is important to bear in mind that deaf-blind or multiply handicapped children may take a different route to achieve the same goals. For example, the Callier Azusa Scale lists the following items as the first five stages in dressing and undressing skills:

o Lies passively during dressing; does not respond to dressing or undressing.
1 Resists being undressed or dressed, cries, attempts to turn over, kicks.
2 Is somewhat less resistant to being undressed and dressed.
3 Assists in undressing if prompted; co-operates in dressing.
4 Initiates some undressing activities; assists in dressing.

We would expect all our children to reach the stage of being able to assist in dressing and to initiate some undressing activities. The child will probably have to have been shown, co-actively, how to achieve the skill, and he may therefore have followed a different method from the non-handicapped child in attaining the goal, but he will have successfully completed the task, nevertheless.

Some observational reports, in particular, are designed to assist Local Education Authorities to decide which is the most appropriate school or further education placement for a particular child. Up to the age of two, most children's placements are within their own home, although some will attend special nurseries if it is thought desirable by parents and involved professionals. In some areas of the country opportunities for schooling start at age two, whilst other children will not go to school until the term after their fifth birthday. This may be governed by parental choice, by professional assessment of the child's needs, or by the availability of provisions in the child's locality. Children may attend a nursery, opportunity playgroup, school or child development and assessment centre until they go into full-time education. Schools which may be thought of as suitable for multiply handicapped or deaf-blind children are those for children with severe learning difficulties, schools for visually impaired children, hearing impaired children, language disordered children, and specialist deaf-blind units. Of the few deaf-blind units currently available in this country only one is attached to a day school; the others are attached to schools for visually impaired and hearing impaired children. At the time of writing (1986) there are four units for deaf-blind adults in this country although very many adults would benefit from these specialist facilities. Many deaf-blind or multiply handicapped young people will leave specialist units where they have had a high staff-to-child ratio and, instead of being able to move on to further education within adult deaf-blind units, will instead be offered a place in an adult training centre for mentally handicapped people or for adults with one disability (deafness or blindness). This situation is very gradually improving, and there are plans for a variety of further educational opportunities, but there is still a long way to go. In order to help improve services for deaf-blind young people, it is necessary for all informed professionals to carry on a dialogue and support each other so that national provisions can be planned as the need arises.

Services often depend to a large extent on the changing needs of particular areas, and within each area the strength of the voices of concerned parents and involved professionals can help towards achieving specialist provision. One of the ways professional people can help parents is to support them in their efforts as a group, and to help them to see that an ideal service can and should always be aimed for within their own area. This ideal service should provide completely for the individual and changing needs of each family and should recognise that these families may have different needs at different times in their child's life. Parents' groups may need help in presenting a unified and comprehensive approach in leading the way within their own area. The priorities of parents are usually the priorities of professionals: comprehensive plans and services for a particular child, group of children, family or groups of families need to be provided, which will monitor the changing needs of the children and their families. Groups must learn to work together, to review current needs, and to evolve strategies to give each other support.

3 Deaf-Blind Children

There is no clear definition of deaf-blindness that will satisfy all the involved professionals. Equally, there is no one disease or syndrome which can now be described as being the main cause of deaf-blindness. Before the rubella vaccination programme began to take effect in the 1980s, rubella (or German measles, as it is more commonly called) was the major known cause of deaf-blindness, but children with congenital rubella syndrome are fortunately no longer being born in the large numbers of the 1950s and 1960s, and much can now be done to help the few cases that occur.

As is well known, rubella, when contracted by the mother in early pregnancy, can be the cause of deafness, blindness and associated heart conditions, as well as a variety of physical disorders. The eye can be affected in many ways, including microphthalmos (very small eyes), permanent scarring of the cornea, cataracts, congenital glaucoma and ocular movements such as nystagmus. Cardiovascular malformations can include: patent ductus arteriosus, transposition of the great arteries, tetralogy of Fallot, ventricular septal defect, hypoplasia of the abdominal aorta and pulmonary arterial stenoses. The rubella damaged child may have sensori-neural deafness and there may be associated physical disabilities and bone disorders.

The important point about children damaged by rubella is that they may have a combination of all three major handicapping conditions. They do, however, have one advantage over all other children known to be deaf-blind: because they have been diagnosed as rubella damaged, their chances of receiving the right attention at the right time are greatly increased, since paediatricians and those who care for the young child have a

heightened awareness of the possibility of additional handicaps and should therefore diagnose these and treat them very
early. Rubella damaged children are known to have a strong
possibility of having hearing and sight problems which can
vary and often deteriorate, so that the aware professional will
monitor the child's performance very carefully and will alert
his parents to the need for regular eye and ear tests.

Whilst the physical effects of congenital rubella syndrome
are well documented and indisputable, some of the behaviour
disorders that have been associated with these children should
be reconsidered. Having worked with many rubella damaged
children, I feel that some theories about behaviour disorders and feeding problems which have been associated
with congenital rubella syndrome should be radically altered. I
am currently working with many young rubella damaged
children who have a combination of handicapping conditions,
such as a severe to profound hearing loss, cataracts and severe
heart defects corrected by surgery. The common factor in most
of these rubella damaged children is the absence of the be-
havioural difficulties apparent in older rubella damaged children, and I can only conclude that this is due to the early
intervention programmes which have become available.

In most of the literature describing children handicapped by
rubella, we read about the 'typical' rubella child's behaviour:
light-gazing, eye-poking, head-banging, random hand movements, finger-flicking, tripoding (walking with hands and feet
on the floor and never gaining an upright position) and severe
feeding difficulties. The fact that these children are now identified early means that they can often be fitted with hearing aids
when they are very young, and they are often able to wear
contact lenses while they are still small babies. I am convinced
that the fitting of hearing aids, glasses or contact lenses when
the child is young has contributed in large measure to the
success of these children, as have the early intervention programmes that teachers for the hearing impaired and visually
handicapped can now offer, together with the help available
from specialist child development clinics and centres such as
ours. I feel that 'blindisms' and associated mannerisms wit-

nessed in children who have not been given early treatment may be due to lack of stimulation and handling in the child's crucial early years.

The progress of the children described in the following pages, all of whom have congenital rubella syndrome, illustrates the importance of early intervention.

Leigh

Leigh is 18 months old and has been known to the Family Service since he was five months old. At the time of referral he had had bi-lateral cataracts removed and contact lenses fitted. He had had no complications with the lenses, which his mother removed every night, and, when he came to us, was looking at faces and sometimes making eye contact. A hearing loss was suspected when he was a few months old and he was issued with hearing aids at the age of 11 months. Leigh has no behaviour or feeding problems and explores familiar and unfamiliar environments visually as well as by touch.

He walked freely at 15 months, but he was very floppy as a young baby and, because of this, we encouraged his parents to help him move and change his position as often as possible. We recommended that he should lie on his tummy so that he would learn to use his head to look at objects from that position. We started early visual training as soon as he was referred, and at 18 months he is picking up objects as small as saccharin tablets, and is able to step over or around objects and up steps without hesitating. Leigh's walking is very sure: he can move from sitting to crawling and kneels without support, but he prefers to walk, and has begun to walk, with one hand held, up and down stairs. He is able to use a chair in order to reach inaccessible objects.

His parents see the value of the total communication approach, and Leigh has a few natural gestures of his own as well as ten signs which it is clear he understands. He makes a variety of noises and expresses his desire to take part in activities with his parents. Since being issued with hearing aids he will turn towards a voice, and his babbling is increasing every day. All his self-help and social skills are within normal developmental limits. He can spoon feed and finger feed and hold a cup; he enjoys being bathed and will hold out his hands for the towel. He tries to put jumpers on over his head and will put his arms in the sleeves without being shown the sleeve, and he can take off his shoes.

Ruth

Ruth is two-and-a-half years old and is functioning well within normal developmental limits. She has been known to the Family Service for 18 months. At the time of referral she was known to be severely partially sighted, to have feeding problems and a severe sensori-neural hearing loss, and she showed signs of having some of the behaviour problems associated with rubella handicapped children. All these behaviour problems have disappeared:

— light gazing and over-attention to bright, shiny objects;
— lack of interest in eye contact from adults;
— feeding difficulties;
— random hand movements.

Ruth had been fitted with post-aural hearing aids and was visited once a week by a teacher of the hearing impaired, who referred her to our services so that the family could have more help. We are finding that very many teachers of the hearing impaired and visually handicapped are referring young children to our services, since they have the confidence to approach outside agencies if they feel that these will help them to work more effectively with these children.

Ruth's major need at the time of referral was to be helped to look at people and objects other than light reflecting ones. We agreed to visit her home regularly, arranging to be there when her teacher of the hearing impaired or physiotherapist was present, so that we could exchange ideas and information about Ruth's progress and her changing needs.

A summary of Ruth's developmental level shows that we can forecast that her educational needs will be met in a school for mildly handicapped children, or in a school for children who are hearing impaired, provided that either of these schools is able to use a total communication approach (this will be described in greater detail in Chapter 7). Ruth's behaviour is that of a child with a severe hearing loss combined with severe visual impairment. She looks closely at objects, shows very little response to sound and needs to have a familiar, structured routine so that she feels secure. She demonstrates sequences of events.

Gross Motor Skills

Ruth is walking with a slightly unsteady gait; she falls only rarely and is never upset about it. She can get from floor sitting to standing unsupported and is climbing well onto furniture. She climbs stairs on her hands and knees unsupported. Without falling, she is able to bend from standing to pick up an object from the floor. She turns somersaults spontaneously from a kneeling position.

Fine Motor Skills

Ruth is tolerant of having her hands held and guided. She uses a thumb-index finger pincer grip to pick up small objects and looks closely at what she is doing with her hands. She can open each door of the Fisher-Price Shape Sorter appropriately (they are each hinged on a different side), using her index finger, and will attempt to use her index fingernail to prise open the lid of a container. She spontaneously reaches with two hands to pick up a large object, and with one hand to pick up small objects.

Ruth can feed herself chopped-up foods, which she eats scooping with a spoon or stabbing with a fork. She will hold a biscuit while she eats it. She can drink from a cup.

Ruth has always mouthed objects, and although this behaviour has been reducing over the past few months, mouthing still continues to provide her with a lot of tactual information. On some occasions, if she is having difficulty opening a container with her hands, she will attempt to do it with her mouth.

Cognitive Skills

Ruth is showing an increasing awareness of where certain favourite objects are to be found. She will, for example, look for her mother's handbag and search in it to find and play with the bunch of keys; she will go to the dining-room door to find the key in it; she will go to the kitchen to look for her cup when she is thirsty; she will go upstairs to rummage in her brother's and sister's toy boxes. She will search to find an object if she has seen it hidden and will unwrap a loose paper parcel to find an object hidden inside.

She will look at and touch a doll's face with interest. Given a container with a lid on, she will often try to ascertain whether or not there is anything inside it before trying to open it (to do this, she looks through clear plastic containers, and shakes opaque ones).

Ruth has made some attempts to scribble with a crayon in imitation, but she prefers to watch an adult scribbling, or to have an adult guide her hand while she holds the crayon.

Her mother reports that Ruth has recently reacted to changes in her bedtime drink routine and has made clear attempts to get her mother to reinstate the usual routine.

Visual Skills

Ruth subjects most objects to close visual scrutiny, usually holding them close to her face and looking at them in a variety of different lights and from a variety of different angles. She enjoys looking closely at pictures or print and will tap at pictures as if trying to remove objects from them. She enjoys watching and touching her own shadow, and watches as her hands move and create moving shadows on the wall or floor.

Ruth scans the area around her visually and has a good memory of where objects are in her vicinity; she can now reach for an object successfully while she is looking in another direction. She has often seen an object the size of a biro or a teaspoon, lying on the floor up to 12 or 15 feet away, and gone to get it. She tracks moving objects in both the horizontal and vertical planes.

Ruth still greatly prefers playing with objects to playing with people, and all the objects she chooses are those which provide a strong visual stimulus, for example shiny metal or plastic, clear objects containing liquid, objects like plastic baskets with an open gridwork pattern, or lines of print on paper.

Auditory Skills

Ruth shows very little response to sounds, although certain patterns have begun to emerge. She does sometimes respond to a human voice within a range of up to 15 feet—by smiling, by momentarily ceasing what she is doing, by suddenly moving away from where she is standing, or by some combination of these three. She shows some recognition of the direction from which the sound has come but does not always turn to familiar noises.

Receptive Communication

Ruth is demonstrating an awareness of familiar routines and is beginning to show displeasure if these routines are broken. Her responses to spoken language are limited, although her parents report that their comment, 'Ruth, time for your bath,' produces a consistent response every evening (she takes her mother's hand and leads her to the stairs).

Ruth can respond appropriately to certain physical cues; for example, during dressing she will lift an arm when it is tapped, and she will sometimes sit down on her chair if her bottom is tapped. Her family have very recently begun to sign co-actively with her at all appropriate times:

up	sit down	play	eat/food	dinner	bath/wash
drink	more	walk	car	toilet	good
sleep	biscuit				

Expressive Communication

Ruth now vocalises during much of the day and is producing a range of sounds, mostly repetitious, including 'a-a-a', 'eh-eh-eh', 'ooo', 'or', 'ma', 'wah-wah', 'eeah', 'mum-mum-mum', 'ungha-ungha'. Over the past two months, she has begun to demonstrate a slightly wider range of intonation while producing these sounds, and is particularly inclined to vocalise when playing with an object, during rough physical play with another person, or when leading him by the hand to show him something. She will use a whole-hand point to indicate a desired object that is out of reach, and will vocalise to get attention.

Multiply handicapped children may have residual vision and a profound hearing loss . . .

. . . or they may be blind with a severe hearing loss.

It is the combination of hearing and visual impairment that is so important to remember.

Ruth will often search for an adult, then take his hand, pull him to another room and place his hand as near as she can manage to the object she desires but cannot reach herself—she will do this, for instance, to have a door opened. If she is particularly enjoying an activity with an adult, she can ask to have the activity repeated in appropriate ways: if her hand has been tickled, she will offer her open palm for more tickling; if she has been bounced up and down on a lap she will move her bottom around for more bouncing. In these repetitive activities Ruth is able to anticipate and wait for short periods, often producing an audible giggle as she waits.

Social Behaviour
Ruth is largely self-contained in her play, although she does enjoy a wide range of 'rough and tumble' play with others if

they initiate the game. She is becoming increasingly aware of the usefulness of other people to get things which she cannot reach, and will go to some lengths to get their co-operation in this. Her mother reports that, over the past few weeks, she has been seeking out familiar people quite deliberately and initiating contact by touching, holding hands or by climbing on their laps. She usually smiles to herself while doing this, and may attempt to make eye contact with the other person involved.

On a number of occasions, Ruth has knocked objects together in imitation of an adult. She is beginning to co-operate in dressing and undressing and will now, for example, raise an arm when it is tapped to have it put in a sleeve, and remove a vest or jumper if it is removed as far as the crown of her head. She is generally very relaxed and happy, even when she is slightly unwell with a cold. She is very exploratory, and will scrutinise an object closely for up to a minute at a time before discarding it to look for a new object. She is showing some signs of becoming more interested in people and, particularly during rough physical play, can sustain interactions with another person.

Priti

Priti is five years old and is functioning well within normal developmental limits. She has been known to the Family Service for 18 months. At the time of referral she was known to be totally blind in her right eye, but with useful partial sight in her left eye, and to have a severe sensori-neural hearing loss; she also manifested some of the behaviour problems associated with rubella handicapped children. All these behaviour problems have disappeared: tripoding (see p. 50), lying on her back and light gazing, finger-flicking and random hand movements.

At the time of referral Priti was in a special care nursery where all the other children were immobile. She was extremely lucky in having both very caring and sensitive nursery nurses and a very helpful home situation, and her parents and nursery nurses were willing to carry out any suggestions to help Priti achieve normal developmental milestones. As part of her programme they agreed that she should visit the Family Centre once a week, for a two-hour developmental play session, always being accompanied by one of her parents or nursery nurses so as to ensure continuity of approach.

The first major alteration we had to achieve was to show Priti that the world was more interesting in an upright position than from a prone or tripod position. We therefore encouraged her to use gross motor skills on a circuit (see p. 117). Once in an upright position, Priti's vision and fine movements were trained and, throughout her programme, we used a co-active signing approach (see p. 132) to give her the ability to communicate with family, adults in the nursery and peers. Priti's educational needs will now be met by a school for deaf children with additional handicaps, rather than inappropriate placement in a school for mentally handicapped children. As with Ruth, when reading the summary of Priti's developmental level it is important to note that her visual and auditory skills show that her teachers have to pay close attention to these areas in any programme which they devise.

Gross Motor Skills

Priti walks with a slightly unsteady gait. She is able to run in an unconfined flat space, occasionally falling over. She climbs onto furniture, walks up and down stairs and gets up and down a slide unaided; she shows some awareness of danger during these activities but is still likely to bump herself or fall. She enjoys being lifted, swung through the air, thrown up and down and swung upside down by an adult. She likes to play on all large playground equipment (swings, slides, roundabouts and climbing frames) and will often do this unaided.

Priti can kick a football from a standing position, although she has no idea of aiming yet. She does aim quite well in ball-rolling games with an adult, although she often fails to use sufficient force in rolling the ball for it to reach the adult.

She can turn a somersault unaided. She enjoys knocking a balloon up into the air and then chases it to knock it up again. She is able to throw small wooden blocks into a 14-inch diameter bucket about two-and-a-half feet away, getting about two out of every three blocks into the bucket.

Vision and Fine Motor Skills

Priti can scoop dry rice with a sand spade or spoon and, with some spillage, tip it into a container. She can stack ten one-inch blocks. She enjoys painting and scribbling with crayons: she scribbles spontaneously both horizontally and vertically, in zig-zags and circles, and frequently changes colour. During painting sessions she often rinses her brush in water before changing colour, and when using felt-tip pens she removes and replaces the caps on the pens spontaneously. She will scribble in imitation of an adult and is attempting to trace around templates in imitation. Priti is very interested in cutting paper with an adult, using training scissors.

Priti enjoys blowing bubbles with a Blowmaster pipe, but needs an adult's help to stop her sucking the bubbles back into the pipe again. She is able to 'pop' bubbles using a gentle index finger point. She also enjoys holding large bubbles in her wet hands, and is very amused at being able to stretch and squeeze them. Apart from bubbles, she also enjoys a wide variety of other tactile substances which she feels with great interest— dry rice, dry pasta, water, rice and washing-up liquid mix. When playing with play-doh she will knead and roll it, try to cut it with a knife and poke her finger to make holes in it.

She spontaneously threads large beads using a long-stemmed threader. Whilst replacing inset puzzle pieces, she often experiences difficulty in manoeuvring them into their holes; she pays close visual attention but tries to push the pieces in using her whole hand rather than lifting them by their handles and placing them in.

Self-Help Skills

Priti can take herself to the toilet and manages the whole routine unaided, although she needs reminding to flush the toilet and to wash her hands. She can wash her hands quite well but usually needs reminding to use soap; while washing her hands she often gives her face a token wash spontaneously. She drinks from a cup and eats well, jabbing or scooping with a fork, or scooping with a spoon. If given a knife, she will attempt (unsuccessfully) to cut food with it. She looks for a tissue and wipes her nose with it spontaneously. Priti can dress and undress with adult intervention and encouragement, but needs help with zips, buttons and sandal straps. If left to her own devices she can usually find her way into her clothes, although they are sometimes back to front or inside out.

Cognitive Skills
Priti enjoys symbolic play with dolls and a tea-set, but prefers to play at this alone, without adult involvement. Occasionally, however, she has brought an adult to sit and play with her. She will spontaneously place dolls on chairs, then bring the tea-set to them and proceed to organise a tea party. Her spontaneous pretend play with a tea-set is impressive; she will place a cup, saucer and spoon together and a knife, fork and plate together, pour from a teapot into the cup, spoon 'sugar' from the sugar bowl into the cup and stir it, spoon 'food' from a large bowl onto a plate and then pretend to eat it using a knife and fork. She includes the dolls in this and will offer them 'food' and 'drink'.

With pictorial inset puzzles she is now recognising a growing number of pieces and demonstrating this in a variety of ways—she pushes a lorry piece along the table saying 'boom, boom'; she puts a cup piece to her mouth as if to drink, or touches it and says 'hot'; she attempts to turn the dial on the telephone piece or places it to her ear and says 'hello'; other pieces, such as 'dolly', 'book', 'ball', she simply names.

Priti enjoys playing with inset boards and learns through repetition where the pieces go. She has completely mastered a four-piece geometric formboard on her third attempt; with more complex puzzles she usually persists, using a trial and error approach, until the puzzle is completed.

Priti enjoys a lot of 'cause and effect' toys, and will watch an adult carefully in order to imitate him and make the toy work herself—she can turn a key to wind and operate a clockwork toy and can switch on a variety of battery-operated toys.

Priti demonstrates her understanding of many objects by

use. She knows items of clothing, and uses correctly a dustpan and brush, toothbrush, handkerchief, vacuum cleaner, talcum powder and skin cream, hairbrush and comb, tissues, items of cutlery and crockery. She is also recognising many objects from photographs or drawings in books and will spontaneously point at them as she names them.

Communication and Speech
Expressive language. Priti has a spontaneous vocabulary of about sixteen words. These words are almost always used appropriately, except on certain occasions when she is clearly deriving pleasure from rehearsing some of the words she knows—she will break off from playing and slowly say a few words to herself, smile broadly and then carry on where she left off with her play. The same is true of the ten signs she has learnt.

She will use a word or a sign (or both combined) as a communicative device. For example, she will ask for a biscuit using the word and the sign combined, and gets quite upset if this does not produce the desired response from the adult concerned; on at least two occasions she has asked an adult to sit down with her by tapping at his hands and then signing 'sit down', she is often the first to say 'hello' on meeting an adult, and on one occasion has waved and said 'bye' to an adult just as he was about to leave her.

Receptive language. Priti can respond appropriately to a number of spoken questions or commands without any contextual clues: 'Priti, let's take your coat off' (she begins to remove her coat); 'Priti, do you want a drink?' (she goes and sits at the table); 'Priti go and give this to Mummy'; 'Priti, put the pens in the box.' She understands a larger number of statements if they are accompanied by gestures or signs, although she often misses these clues if she is still not paying close visual attention to the people around her. Her responses to adult speech are very inconsistent and she often appears not to hear at all if she is already absorbed in an activity.

Auditory Skills

Priti enjoys a wide range of noise-making toys ranging from a rattle to an electric organ. She will often hold a musical box or an electronic siren up to her ear and rock in time with the sound; on some occasions, while doing this, she has also attempted to vocalise in imitation of the sound she hears. She will sometimes repeat a word she has heard, for example 'push', 'scissors', 'baby', 'cat'.

Priti once stilled in her play to listen to a clock ticking; she searched to find the source of this sound but was unable to locate it and had to be shown. She will sometimes turn when her name is called, especially when it is called by her mother or father.

When given a portable cassette recorder, she will vocalise at it and then give it to an adult to have it played back for her; she listens to recordings of her voice with great pleasure and amusement.

Social skills

Priti does not normally pay very close visual attention to other people, although she recognises a number of people on sight. She uses other people as tools to help her if she cannot manage a task: she will take an adult's hand to the handle of a door she cannot open, or she will give an adult a box to open if she cannot manage it. With her parents, she will often bring a toy to show them. Priti will follow an adult's pointing finger and, if she is sufficiently interested in an activity, will pay close attention to an adult to see how it is done. Through this close attention and imitation she has learnt how to do a number of things very quickly—to blow on a kazoo, trace around a stencil, turn on a toy siren.

If Priti gets upset it is usually possible to distract her attention and get her interested in some form of play activity. She shows signs of anticipating certain routine activities and is beginning to get the idea of putting a toy away before she starts to play with another one, although she often still needs prompting to do this.

Leigh, Ruth and Priti have all been affected by congenital rubella syndrome and, as has been demonstrated, they all have in common a sight and hearing loss which has resulted in severe learning difficulties. These difficulties have largely been ameliorated because they have had early intervention and treatment from members of the medical and educational professions as well as from relevant therapists. However, whereas it is relatively easy to diagnose the sight and hearing defects of rubella damaged children, it is often much more difficult to recognise that some children will have a combination of sight and hearing loss when they are older.

There are countless diseases and syndromes which can be associated with deaf-blindness, including those, such as Usher's Syndrome, which may have serious genetic implications, and there are probably as many causes as yet unidentified and therefore unknown. Meningitis and encephalitis are illnesses which can cause the sighted/hearing child to lose these faculties.

If a child has had normal sight and hearing even for a few months, that child has still had experiences of sight and sound which he may retain and which can help him to learn, particularly if he has had some experience of speaking. Helen Keller was such a child. She lost her sight and hearing when she was less than two years old and, although she must always be thought of as a remarkable woman of keen intelligence, she did not have to face what most deaf-blind children have to overcome. They, from birth, do not have normal exposure to sight or sound and often, for the first few months of their lives, may be deprived of normal bonding experiences with their parents. They may have been born in a distressed state, been premature or have obvious physical signs of abnormality, so that they are immediately subjected to special care and treatment. We are now learning how important early bonding is, and many special care or premature baby units make marvellous provision for the parents and ensure that they handle and care for their babies as soon as possible. Other hospitals do not.

If the child goes home soon after birth and is then discovered to be handicapped, it is often the parents and grandparents who have the first anxiety that something is wrong with their baby. However much the parents love and care for their child, hearing 'bad news' about him can never be easy, and it may be several weeks or months before they are able to come to terms with their child's condition. It is in these crucial early weeks and months that so much emotional damage to parents and children can take place.

A major problem caused by having a multiply handicapped child is that diagnosis can be time-consuming, traumatic and difficult and may involve dozens of hospital visits before the child's parents have a clear picture of his needs and the treatment he requires. With some children, it may only be when they are nearing school age that any definite diagnosis can be achieved, because only when they have become mobile or have started to develop some social skills is it obvious that they have a serious sight or hearing condition. Unless the blind child develops speech at a normal age it is always difficult to assess whether or not he is hearing normally, since blind children do not turn to sound. They may 'still' to sound or alter their facial expression, but they do not turn as a sighted baby will. In a test situation, most audiologists use games, such as getting a child to put a brick in a box or a man in a boat every time he hears the sound. This method is usually inappropriate for the blind child and, unless the audiologist is prepared to use other observational methods, he will get a very distorted picture of the blind child's ability to hear.

The hearing of many partially sighted children is as difficult to assess as the blind child's, since they are so visually aware that they tend to ignore environmental sounds or sounds that have no meaning for them. Many older rubella damaged children, for example, are fascinated by light and will gaze at fluorescent lights or the nearest light source, usually the window. If the rubella damaged child's hearing is tested in a brightly lit room and account is not taken of his obsession with light, then a true assessment of his hearing will usually not be obtained. Unless the partially sighted child has speech, it is very difficult indeed to assess exactly what he can see, for it is only through words that he can describe his visual limits and capabilities. A deaf child would therefore find it hard to express how much or how little he could see.

With the multi-handicapped child the problems of assessment of vision and hearing are even greater. Suffice to say that the earlier the diagnosis takes place, the earlier the right treatment can be started. It would be a costly but extremely worthwhile task if every Health Authority could set up a systematic referral procedure, so that all children known to be blind or partially sighed could go to a specialist audiologist who had an interest in testing them, and all children known to be deaf or partially hearing could attend a specialist ophthalmologist who had an equivalent interest. Thus, in each area of the country there would be efficient and speedy diagnosis as well as an increasingly expert team of people able to give advice and information as early as possible. When a child has a combination of handicaps, even a *slight* loss can become a serious extra handicapping condition. If a blind child has Eustachian tube blockage or 'glue-ear' he may be unable to make sense of his world. If a deaf child needs to wear glasses and they have not been issued to him, then he cannot function at his optimum capacity.

Fundamental to the child's ability to learn is the treatment he requires, and this can only be achieved by the global assessment of his needs as a whole child. So often a child is seen by different specialists for separate conditions; if he is to receive the right treatment, he must be seen as a developing individual with special needs and should attend a centre which can co-ordinate all his necessary treatment programmes. There are some extremely good child development centres which can provide specialist help for our children, in which their medical, educational, social and therapy needs will be planned for. And likewise, there are children who have received very little in the way of treatment, whose parents feel that they have had little or no support in the child's early years. Where the services are co-ordinated, the professionals will see the children and their parents as individuals and will ensure that the parents understand the complex needs of their children. They will help the parents to tackle their problems and will share the care of the multiply handicapped child.

4 Zachary

Zachary is the only son of a single mother who decided when she was pregnant that she would not keep him, so he went straight from the hospital to a children's home to await adoption. It was in the children's home that it was discovered that he was blind. Zachary's diagnosis is retinopathy of prematurity, and he had persistent glue-ear, resulting in severe conductive deafness. The children's home was staffed by warm, responsive adults. There were seven other children there, none of them handicapped.

This, in some ways, would have seemed an ideal placement for Zachary, but unfortunately it was not. He is totally blind and, because of his persistent ear infections (and consequent hearing impairment), was completely unable to understand the normal activities that surrounded him. He responded by withdrawing into his own self-stimulatory behaviour and, whilst he received a great deal of affectionate handling, his progress was very slow indeed. At the time when the peripatetic advisory teacher from the Family Advisory Service first met him, he was aged two years and had proved difficult to place for adoption because of his handicaps; it was felt by some workers that he was mentally handicapped and that he might have other damage as his muscles were so floppy.

On his referral at the age of two, Zachary was extremely timid, panicking if he was left alone. He quite clearly had no idea about his environment, behaved in an extremely insecure fashion and was 'alarmed' by being jostled even in the gentlest manner. He was unable to sit up unsupported, neither did he reach out for a sound-making toy. He presented as a very severely handicapped child. He had very few noticeable signals, although he did appear to respond to cuddling by nestling his body closer to the adult who was cuddling him.

Zachary did not appear to localise sound even in a groping or trial and error manner, and he had no clear anticipation of the next movement in any normal routines such as feeding or toileting. He did not appear to copy any movements, signals or sounds, even when given to him repeatedly by his most familiar adult. He did not appear to listen to an adult's vocalisation, nor did he attend to a variety of sound-making toys. He would not permit his hands, feet or body to be moved over unfamiliar or familiar surfaces, and he would not explore any object with his fingers. He did not appear to know that he could turn objects over or that his fingers belonged to him—he had no exploratory behaviour. He was frightened of water, screamed when he was put in the bath, would not splash his hands in the water, nor did he appear to gain any enjoyment from the experience of being bathed. He had no tolerance to sand or other so-called tactile materials and withdrew from all soft-textured materials. He was entirely passive, apparently unaware that his limbs were being touched or manipulated and, although he would allow tactile stimulation of each limb (rubbing, stroking, tickling), he made no apparent movements to indicate whether he enjoyed or disliked the experience. When given a selection of toys to play with he made no moves towards them. Taken outside, he was extremely fearful and would not handle or sit on the grass.

Zachary had attended a child development centre and had been diagnosed (labelled) as totally blind with a significant hearing loss, and mentally handicapped with possible other damage. The main recommendation was that he should receive physiotherapy *once a week*. Fortunately his physiotherapist, having worked successfully with the Family Advisory Service with another child, decided that it might be helpful to refer him to our services, which she accordingly did.

On first meeting Zachary, we spent a great deal of time discussing his need to establish bodily signals, which we felt he could achieve through play activities. As he had no sight, we felt that it was vital to impress on his physiotherapist the need to increase his communication, and for everyone within the children's home to work in the same way, so that he could learn to associate everyday activities with pleasure rather than fear. We discussed Zachary's need to listen to and attend to the variety of sounds he was experiencing within his environment and that he should be helped to search for and localise these sounds. We felt that he needed to understand where the sounds were coming from and that they all had meaning, and that one of the reasons why he was so passive was that he had no understanding of his environment—things were happening to him but not with him, and he had not as yet developed the ability to listen. We asked the physiotherapist, with the co-operation of the staff of the children's home, to count the number of adults whom Zachary encountered each day, and were not surprised to discover that there were eight different adults with whom he must learn to interact, as well as the seven other children. His defence had been to withdraw.

It is interesting to look back on the label that Zachary had been given. Had he been labelled as mentally handicapped because he was unresponsive to the environment? Had he been labelled as mentally handicapped because he was not bab-bling, and had his conductive deafness been taken into account? Had he been labelled as mentally handicapped without thought to the environmental influences which impinged on his behaviour? It is extremely difficult for the blind child with a hearing difficulty to attend to the things that he can neither see nor hear clearly, so he had reacted quite normally by cutting out what he did not understand or want to hear. He had been given no opportunities to organise his hearing; he had no incentive to remember or recognise, to associate or discriminate one person from another. He was able neither to receive nor to give information, he had no one with whom to reciprocate and no one to interpret his world for him. Nothing was meaningful, no sound had been localised for him, and he did not know who was talking to him or what was about to happen. He had no one with whom he had been able to build up a warm and trusting emotional bond and had been unable, because of his hearing loss, to understand the words he heard.

Because he was in an environment with sighted/hearing children, he had not been given the normal explanations about his environment which he would have received had he been getting specialised help.

We felt it was important to impress upon the people working with Zachary that he should have one-to-one ratio as far as possible; without this it was impossible to see whether or not he was going to be able to develop any speech or language, or whether we should start to think about him communicating through signing. We helped the staff to compile suitable activities for Zachary which included as much time for intensive play (see p. 113) as they were able to allow and decided, with their co-operation, to reduce the number of adults he met to two, so that he could learn to identify them individually. We listed activities to help develop his auditory, tactile, motor and self-help skills. We felt that his communication skills would only develop by being used, and that it was important for the staff to realise that he needed clear explanations about what was happening to him; they should base all their work with Zachary on what they already knew about normal child development, and should allow him to dictate the content, course and pace of their interactions with him. As Zachary was so passive, we felt it was extremely important that, within his intensive play activities, the staff should be helped to see that his bodily signals, however minute, should always be acknowledged, and that they should create for him the understanding that any action of his would get a response from them. We decided that his intensive play should constantly repeat the same actions, so that he would gradually learn to expect a certain pattern of movement and might then react to it.

Zachary had appeared to be something of a mystery to the staff in the children's home because he had behaved in all respects as a profoundly deaf child as well as being totally blind, and they had behaved to him as though he was also profoundly mentally handicapped. This had meant that in many ways their speech had been extremely limited and confined to conversations about bodily functions such as toileting, bathing and dressing. Once the staff had initiated the play activities a dramatic change took place. He began to giggle and laugh when his two workers indicated that it was time for an intensive play session. He began to pivot (turn) on his bottom when he was sitting, and could hold on to furniture when standing. He began to grasp small objects, and would sometimes drop them purposely and then pick them up and manipulate them. He began using several speech-like sounds such as 'daddee', 'babee', 'mamee' and 'a-ee'.

Encouraged by Zachary's obvious progress, the staff were now excited by the idea of working with him and asked for more ideas to help his postural control and locomotion, his fine motor skills and communication skills; this we were happy to supply.

*   *   *

Play Activities for Zachary (aged three)

Postural Control and Locomotion
Zachary can pivot (turn) on his bottom when he is sitting; he can hold onto furniture when standing and he can walk using a 'walker'. Much of his ability to move forward or sideways when he is standing depends on his attitude towards it. He gets very cross/unsure of himself when he is asked to stand and walk forward. Because he does not want to practise this skill, he does not gain enough confidence to know that he can do it. He needs to *want* to pull up from sitting to standing and to be motivated towards rising from a kneeling position to standing. Try using his interest in food or his interest in noise-making toys to act as inducements to move forwards and sideways. He needs to stand *alone* for a few seconds without support, with his arms out at shoulder level for balance. Try putting him between two chairs with an interesting sound-making toy on each chair.

Zachary must feel safe for this activity, so the chairs should be close enough for him to feel their presence but not so close that he is leaning on them. When he gets used to the idea of standing (with an adult supporting him) and playing with toys,

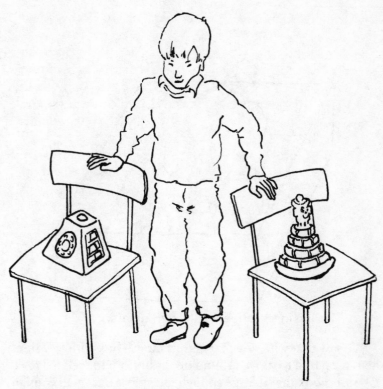

Standing between two chairs, each with an interesting sound-making toy.

the chairs could gradually be moved further away, so that eventually he is reaching further and further for his toys. It is likely that he will quite accidentally stand unsupported for a few seconds while taking part in this activity.

Zachary gets into a 'bear crawl' posture and will probably start to explore his environment using this mode of loco-motion. Can you encourage his mobility by crawling alongside him and showing him items of interest in the house and garden? He needs to know the names of everything he meets. He allows himself to be held upright both from in front and behind; he also needs practice in being held (both with his arms up and down) with an adult standing on each side of him.

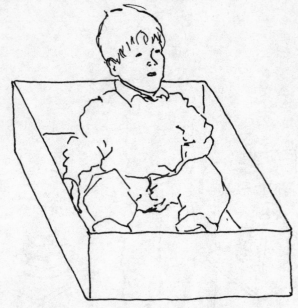

Sitting in a box feeling the perimeters.

We saw that when Zachary is in a largish box with low sides he is prepared to move around on his bottom to seek for toys. Choose a box that is large enough to explore but small enough for him to find the perimeters, so that it gives him a feeling of security. You have obviously done a great deal of work with Zachary sitting on your knee, putting him in different positions, rocking him backwards and forwards, etc. He is now prepared to move his body in space and can use his body muscles and counteract the momentary loss of balance. It would be a good idea to continue this activity so that he builds on the skills acquired.

Fine Motor Skills
Zachary can grasp and purposely drop an object, pick up objects and manipulate them, turning them over to examine them, move his fingers in many directions and is prepared to 'look at' objects which are soft as well as hard. He does not reject materials which have a variety of textures and is adventurous in the way he approaches new objects. He needs to learn

to handle smaller and more intricate (cause and effect) toys/ objects/materials. He can take objects out of a container. He now needs to learn to put objects in and out of the same container, to dump objects out of a container and put them into the same container, to take objects out of one container and transfer them to another and to 'post' objects in a container such as a coffee tin with a lid. He can learn to take the lid on and off in order to get an object such as a biscuit. He should be encouraged to take an interest in sand and water, and to seek for toys in the sand and water. After he has learnt to do this he can be encouraged to pour sand and to pour water.

Auditory Skills
Zachary uses several speech-like sounds such as 'daddee', 'ee', 'baba', 'dada', 'ahah', 'emem', 'mamer', 'naner' and apparently calls himself 'Aki'. It is extremely important to respond to these babbles by imitating them when you are quite close to him, so that he can feel your face. We noted he always uses his *left* ear in preference to his right to listen to toys, and he searches/localises with his left ear. He enjoys using sound-making toys such as a drum and a xylophone and can search for rattles and the RNIB ball when they are removed to a distance of eighteen inches.

You are using certain key phrases which you are accompanying with signs. As you know, it is extremely important to speak to Zachary about everything in clear, simple sentences.

Transferring objects from one container to another.

Because he appears to have some useful hearing, we should work to increase his listening skills by presenting him with a variety of sound-making toys, giving him toys that he can bang and shake, encouraging him to copy rhythms and to 'listen out' for his favourite toys before they are given to him. It is most important to ensure that Zachary receives as much auditory information as possible at this vital stage.

*   *   *

Although Zachary was continuing to make very good progress, he was still significantly delayed in his development—particularly in his physical development, as he was not yet standing and walking, and also in speech and the understanding of language. We felt that the deficit in speech and language was of special concern, because if he was going to make further progress it would depend on whether he could hear and interpret speech.

At that time Zachary had a hearing test. It was felt that he had a hearing loss in both ears of approximately 65 decibels. The impedence audiometry showed that there was little movement of the timpanic membrane and no measurable middle ear pressure point, which was indicative of fluid in the middle ear cavity. Until this problem was resolved, it was felt that it would be very difficult to establish whether or not he had an underlying sensori-neural impairment.

During the next few months he made so much progress that it was clear to us that his mental ability was probably that of a normal child, and that his delay (apart from speech) could be entirely accounted for by the lack of bonding which had previously occurred. Now that he was able to demonstrate to the staff that he was capable of learning, his programme altered to take into account his new mobility and fine motor skills. We still felt that language was the key to his whole further development.

*   *   *

Play Activities for Zachary (aged three years six months)

Motor Development

Zachary can pull himself to standing, cruise around furniture, crawl forward towards a sound-making toy, will hold on to (but does not like) a walker, will hold on to a hand and will walk with people if he feels secure. As he is totally blind (with no light perception) his main need, now that he is able to negotiate furniture, is to gain in confidence. This can only be achieved through practice, and by realising that some objects are safe to hold on to and that some will move. He should not be given a walker unless you are sure there is someone to guide this, from in front. We feel that it is far better for him to practise the art of mobility by letting him explore the environment through any means that he chooses: crawling, cruising, rolling, holding hands. When you are with him it is always a good idea to identify the environment for him:

—Zachary, the chair is here
—Zachary, let's open the door
—Zachary, let's play on the grass

NOTE: Always say his name first, so that Zachary knows *you are talking to him*. This will get his attention.

He needs to know everything about his environment, and only you can supply the information. General points about his mobility include that he should always walk *to* someone and not *away* from them, or he should walk at someone's side with *one* hand held. He needs practice in standing alone; he should be given the opportunity to stand and play at a table, at a sand tray, by a person. He should not be expected to stand alone yet, as he needs to know the points of reference in a room first before he moves freely. (From his point of view he loses security if he feels he is unsupported—because of his total blindness he needs to feel that he is standing near something supportive that will not 'move away' unexpectedly.) A trampoline will help give him the experience of movement.

Zachary can overcome obstacles when he is crawling and does not mind bumping into furniture occasionally. It is important to bear in mind that he probably does not appreciate the dimensions of furniture, and that when he is standing or walking they may appear to be entirely different and probably quite frightening. He should therefore be given opportunities to explore all around and behind the furniture so that he recognises it from an upright position.

Self-Help Skills

Zachary can take off socks, shoes, a scarf and a hat and will pull on mittens. He should now be helped co-actively (from behind, hand over hand) to take off and put on all his clothes. Naturally you will show him each garment as he puts it on and will praise all his efforts at dressing/undressing himself. It is very important that he should only dress/undress when it is appropriate: he should not formally 'learn' to dress/undress at this stage. During the summer months there are many opportunities for him to take off and put on his clothes when he is playing in the garden.

We agreed that Zachary should learn to use soap and flannel and that he should be given opportunities to learn to clean his teeth. He knows what a brush is and will put it on his head and try to brush his hair; now he should be encouraged to practise this skill (again only at appropriate times in the day).

He eats very well and is feeding himself practically independently. Now that he has a stable tray he will probably find this easier. As we agreed, Zachary needs to learn the skill of drinking from a cup. The action that he uses to drink from his feeding beaker is not helping him to learn to take smaller sips (rather than large gulps!) and we agreed that 50 per cent of his drinks should be taken from a cup, gradually working towards full-time use of the cup.

Fine Motor Skills

Zachary can now be encouraged to investigate toys or objects with moving parts and should be shown co-actively (hand over hand) how to transfer objects from one container to another and how to take lids from containers. When he is learning anything we have to decide if it is *useful* to him, so when he is learning to remove lids he should only do this if there is a purpose behind the activity, such as to get a biscuit or a toy.

Communication

We decided that his main need is to increase his ability to communicate, so that he can indicate his needs or desires more effectively. Zachary has one clear meaningful word—'dow' for down—and a range of other babbles, jargoning and word-like sounds. We decided that one word-like sound, 'ye' for yes, should be made more specific, and that when you feel that he *means* 'yes' he should also nod his head. At other times he should be allowed to say 'ye-ye' in the same way as he says all his other word-like sounds.

Zachary is at quite a vital stage now. When he says, for instance, 'Zazee', you should say something like, 'Hello, Zachary, I can hear you, Zachary, hello.' He needs to know that some of his word-like sounds have meaning so it is important for those words to be identified and expanded and commented on as often as possible.

Try to remember to sequence or order things for Zachary, for instance:

Zachary is coming inside;
Zachary is going to wash his hands;
Zachary is going to sit down;
Zachary is going to eat tea;

rather than, 'Come over here.' As you now understand, you always have to be *quite specific* with any blind child.

REMEMBER

He needs to know that you are talking to him—**identify him by name.**

He needs to know exactly what is going to happen to him —**identify the action and place by name.**

He needs to know who is talking to him—**identify yourself by name.**

Try to think simply, speak in clear, short sentences and sometimes sign the word you mean or show Zachary what you mean through gestures, touch or emotion. We discussed, for instance, that a good strong 'Zachary, NO', and a very happy 'Zachary, GOOD BOY', will often be the phrases which may require the emphasis of signs to help Zachary to understand more clearly the speech he hears. We decided that, even though Zachary has some useful hearing, we would employ the British Sign Language signs to support speech wherever you felt this would help him to understand your conversation more clearly. As you know, he has made progress in all areas since we last made our informal observation/assessment.

*   *   *

At this time, Zachary was placed as a foster child with a couple who had one child, aged three-and-a-half. As Zachary had made so much progress, it could not have been foreseen that he would find his fostering placement so difficult. Hindsight teaches us all things. When he was removed from the children's home to his new foster home, everyone at the children's home was in agreement that this was the best placement for him, since he would be with two loving adults and would have a foster sister; but unfortunately the placement proved disastrous. Zachary lost all his confidence and became extremely vulnerable, very angry and disturbed. Clearly it had not been realised that he had come to rely on his two workers within the children's home, and that he was now so aware of his environment that he would actively miss them. He began to hit and bang himself all the time and once more retreated into his own world. He smacked himself if he wanted something, he smacked himself if he heard the word 'no', he ate in an 'over-compensating' way, he sat on the floor and circled around aimlessly, he rested his fists in his eyes, blew 'raspberries' almost constantly, could not, with so many self-stimulating behaviours, amuse himself and was extremely clinging, needing constant reassurance. It proved impossible for his foster mother and father to cope with the demands of a small child so dependent on them, and at the same time cope with their own three-and-a-half-year-old daughter and her needs, so once more he was returned to the children's home.

He now cried constantly, needing the protection and reassurance of his two main workers who were unable to give him the complete attention he demanded, thus making him even more unhappy. At one stage it was felt that he had regressed so much and manifested so many disturbing and self-destructive habits that he might have to be removed from the children's home, since his behaviour was reacting on the other children in such an adverse way.

Then Zachary was placed for adoption with another couple. His mother did not go out to work and his father worked regularly from Monday to Friday in a nine-to-five job. Zachary's real personality began to emerge. His new mother and father were able to spend a great deal of time helping him to overcome his difficulties as they had no other children.

*   *   *

Review of Progress Six Months after Zachary's Adoptive Placement (aged five)

Emotional Development

When Zachary came to live with you he was in a disturbed state and he exhibited many 'blindisms' and self-stimulating behaviours. For instance he:

—smacked himself if he wanted something;
—smacked himself if he heard the word 'no';
—ate in an 'over-compensating' way;
—sat on the floor and circled around aimlessly;
—rested his fists in his eyes;
—blew 'raspberries' almost constantly;
—could not amuse himself as he had so many self-stimulating behaviours;
—was extremely clinging and needed constant reassurance.

Because you have been able to provide him with a one-to-one ratio, *all* of the self-stimulating behaviours and 'blindisms' have ceased, except when Zachary feels extremely unsure (perhaps in new or noisy surroundings, or with a strange adult). He is now happy, secure and contented with you, bearing in mind the following important points:

—he has to be in a one-to-one adult relationship;
—he must be with adults he knows reasonably well;

—he must not feel in competition with other people (including children, and particularly very young ones);

—he always functions best in quiet, calm, undisturbed surroundings.

He has an excellent relationship with his parents and is beginning to trust again.

Mobility Training
Zachary can now walk freely and confidently in the house, but there must always be someone with him to guard him from danger and to give him the constant reassurance of an adult's presence. He walks up and down stairs, one hand held. He does not walk freely outside but will follow an adult's sound directions (voice or claps) so long as that adult is only one yard away. He is beginning to learn routes, such as from the bathroom to his room and from the swing to the slide. He is beginning to learn how to get down from an adult-sized dining chair and from an adult-sized toilet (with his mother only at this stage).

Self-Care Skills
Feeding. Zachary feeds himself competently using an adult-sized fork and plate where this is appropriate. He can use a teaspoon or dessert spoon, and uses ordinary dishes from which to eat. He finger-feeds foods such as sandwiches, bananas and crisps (and can feel in the bag for crisps). He uses any cup with or without a handle, and can search for it on the table if it has been placed on his right-hand side.

Toileting. Zachary is usually clean and dry throughout the day but has the occasional 'accident'. He uses an adult-sized toilet (with a child's toilet seat). He wears nappies at night. He asks for a 'wee-wee' a 'two-two' or says 'toilet' at appropriate times.

Washing and dressing. Zachary enjoys a bath and accepts the teeth-cleaning process. He tries to dry himself (unsuccessfully). He likes to be clean, although, like all children, he also enjoys getting dirty again! He makes a good attempt at combing his hair. He can pull off most garments with minimal assistance and tries to pull up his pants and trousers. He knows where his clothes are kept and names shoes and socks.

Speech
Zachary knows at least 15 action songs and nursery rhymes and can supply the last word in a sequence. He can name most body parts and is learning to count to ten. He knows the sounds that some common animals make and will imitate police car or siren noises. Although his speech is understandable by his parents and peripatetic advisory teacher, much of it is still indistinct and would not be understood by strangers. He makes frequent reversals—'g' for 'd', 'd' for 'b', 's' for 'f' —which we feel is normal for a developmentally 'young' or hard of hearing child. Zachary's vocabulary increases daily, he can put together three- or four-word sequences and can use words learnt in one situation in another appropriate situation.

Auditory Training
Zachary is being encouraged to listen to sequences of sounds and rhythms, and he has recently started music therapy in order to help his listening skills.

Pre-Braille and Tactual Development
Zachary is starting pre-braille work. Much of this consists of 'looking' at tactile books, scanning and searching different shapes and beginning to trace patterns with his finger. It is planned to label (in braille) certain furniture and toys so that he will be introduced in an incidental way to the 'reading' process.

Swimming and Outdoor Activities
Zachary goes swimming and is very confident in the water, and he is always pleased when it is swimming day. He plays in the garden every day and enjoys the swing, slide and trampoline, but his favourite activity at the moment is to push his trolley. He walks well and has walked, one hand held, for at least a mile.

*   *   *

Throughout this period Zachary's hearing had remained impaired, and it was not until he was placed with his adoptive parents that he had the much-needed medical treatment for his middle ear problem. As soon as he went to live with them he attended an ear, nose and throat hospital and had grommets inserted to drain the fluid from his ears. The results of this minor operation were nothing short of startling! Zachary began to babble. It was quite clear that he began to understand a great deal of speech which he had previously missed. His new adoptive parents understood that communication would be the key to all his further development, but within this he needed activities designed to help him achieve skills in the following areas:
  —mobility training
  —dressing/undressing skills and self-care skills
  —feeding skills
  —toileting development
  —auditory training
  —cognitive skills
  —pre-braille work
  —tactual development
  —informal play and social skills
A summary of the recommendations we made included:

Mobility Training
Because Zachary is totally blind, care will need to be taken that he is given plenty of opportunity to form mental maps of his own home environment before we can expect him to explore unknown locations.

Dressing, Undressing, Self-Care, Feeding and Toileting Skills
Most of his learning will be governed by the need for co-active demonstrations in achieving independence in these areas.

Auditory Training
As Zachary has had years of functioning as a profoundly deaf child, he will need extra help in identifying the environmental sounds which he would, by now, have begun to appreciate had he not had this hearing loss.

Pre-Braille and Tactual Development
Zachary needs to have experience of cause and effect toys because, like so many blind, under-functioning children, he is not fully aware of the use to which he can put his hands and he does not yet explore delicately, nor does he scan. This is vital when he learns braille.

Cognitive Skills and Play Activities
These are interdependent. Without play, no child learns; without help from an understanding adult, the child's cognitive abilities will not be utilised. (As this is such an important area, a whole chapter has been dedicated to the subject —Chapter 8, Structuring the Child's Day for Learning and Play.)

*   *   *

What Can We Learn From Zachary's Story?
The main lesson we have learnt is that no child is helped by being labelled, as far as his intellectual capacities are concerned, unless everyone takes into account the environmental influences that impinge upon him and his development. Zachary was not communicating because he had been taught by circumstances not to communicate. Communication only develops by being used and by being meaningful. Zachary was so confused that, on two separate occasions, he had no option but to withdraw completely. The first time he withdrew, when he was in the children's home, was because the world had no meaning for him. On the second occasion, the world had begun to have meaning and that meaning was withdrawn from him with no explanation; he was taken from the two adults he had learnt to trust and was asked to adapt to a new environment.

The fact that Zachary has managed to overcome his emotionally disturbing start is due to several factors, but must include the fact that his adoptive parents were able to provide a secure emotional environment for him. They agreed that he needed a routine establishing so that he would know exactly what to expect throughout his waking day. We recommended that they should always give him plenty of warning when he was about to change an activity, and that they should look at his behaviour objectively and see that, generally speaking, he had *good* reason for objecting to changes of circumstance. We felt that it was important for them to establish certain routines such as toileting, dressing, washing and feeding, which were always accompanied by the same phrases; this would give Zachary the opportunity to begin to learn to anticipate. When he heard a certain phrase, such as, 'Mummy's going to get your dinner now', he would learn over a period of time that this indeed was the case. As he improved in emotional stability, so his innate intellectual capacity was able to flourish.

Zachary's mother kept a diary and she has kindly allowed me to reproduce part of it, for within it are some important observations on the development of children in general—in particular the need for a secure environment in which they can learn and grow.

Extract 1

Today Zachary played a game of hide and seek with the towel. He took the towel from the towel rail and draped it over his arm, saying, 'Where's your arm Zachary, where's your arm?' then pulled the towel off and said, 'Here it is, here it is.' He repeated this game for several minutes. After some time he elaborated the game by hiding his 'bot-bot', his tummy, his other arm, his hands, his head and his cheeks. He finished the game by saying, 'done, finished the towel.'

Zachary could have played this game without speech but with speech his mother was able to understand that it was a game of hide and seek and that he was not being random in his behaviour.

Extract 2

Zachary can climb upstairs holding on to the banister, hand over hand. He's very pleased with himself, calling himself a clever boy. He is able to turn the corners by kneeling down, retaining a grip on the banister, and then standing up once he feels that his hands are round the corner.

All children need to practise the skills that they have been helped to achieve in their own way, at their own pace.

Extract 3
Zachary is beginning to be able to defer his wants. He asked to play the organ while downstairs and went through the routine formula—'Up the stairs, to the toilet, and then organ time' —without getting cross.

We have encouraged Zachary's parents to use the same phrases for certain routines within his day. This helps Zachary to understand that certain things will always happen, and that he can feel secure in the knowledge that if his mother has said a certain action is about to take place, this is indeed the case.

Extract 4
Yesterday Zachary fell out of bed while I was downstairs making a coffee. He had pushed the safety bars too far while playing a jumping game and fell. When I got upstairs he said (as a cue for me) 'Whatever are you doing there, Zachary?' I repeated the phrase but omitted to say 'Zachary'; he repeated his phrase—'Whatever are you doing there, *Zachary?*'— which I then realised I was also expected to say. Having said this phrase, Zachary then replied, 'Pony ride,' and demonstrated how he had been jumping so that I would understand how he'd fallen.

Extract 5
Last night I asked Zachary whether he would like a sandwich. He appeared to say 'Night night,' so I asked, 'You just want to go to sleep, you don't want a sandwich?' He then explained, 'night night for tea tea, night night sandwiches,' which I then knew meant Marmite sandwiches. It is interesting to see how he is now able to explain himself if I don't quite understand.

Again, language is the key to his mother's understanding. Had Zachary been unable to speak, it would have been important that the signing which we started with him when he was younger should have continued, because in this way he would have been able to demonstrate his needs. Zachary is now able to make clear explanations to his mother so that she can understand him. He knows what communication is, and both

Extract 4 and Extract 5 illustrate the importance of communication through speech and signing.

Extract 6

When Zachary woke in the night he called me (as he always does) and then said, 'Zachary go to sleep,' and fell asleep immediately—normally he waits for me to reply.

Again, see how helpful the formulae have been: because his mother had always replied in the same way, he was able to fall asleep immediately, since he knew that that was what he was expected to do when he awoke during the night.

Extract 7

Zachary stays dry all morning (without nappies—just pants). He has nappies during lunch and for the rest of the day, as he tends to go out in the afternoon.

It is always important to try to maintain routines which the child will understand. It is perfectly acceptable to start toilet training a child in this way: that is, without nappies in the morning and nappies for the rest of the day. The main thing is that the child begins to understand that for some part of the day it is up to him to stay dry, and in fact, by using this method of only having pants in the morning, there was no pressure on Zachary to stay dry completely.

Extract 8

Zachary lost his beater for the xylophone while I was writing this. I told him that the beater was by his right hand, he immediately put out his right hand and found it.

The importance of being able to name body parts cannot be stressed enough. Blind children need to know about their bodies and the ways in which they work. If they are not exposed to this skill then their mobility may well be impaired in the future.

The changing attitudes of people towards Zachary had a great deal to do with his changing abilities. Once he was seen as a child who was capable of learning, and that it was possible to help him to overcome those problems that were occasioned by his total blindness and hearing impairment, he began to develop very quickly.

Zachary's story has been told to illustrate the following points:

—Early 'labelling' is helpful neither to the *child* nor to the *adults* who are working with him.

—Assessments of multiply handicapped children should depend on observational techniques and should take place over a period of time in the environment in which the child is spending the majority of his waking hours (for young children that is usually their home environment).

—Most young blind children who have even a mild hearing loss may not be able to function well in a strange place; they will need time to become adjusted to their environment and to explore this for themselves.

—It is a difficult task to assess any child, it is even more difficult to be the child who is being assessed, particularly when he is nervous or unsure and does not know who is talking to him.

—Everyone who works with a particular multiply handicapped child should be involved in the assessment procedure. This assessment should be produced so that *action* can be taken towards providing an on-going developmental goals for the child.

—Environmental circumstances and past history must be taken into account when assessing children; the way the child has been handled in his early years may always affect his behaviour.

—Hearing loss in a blind child, or poor sight combined with a severe hearing loss, may have serious consequences for the child's educational development.

POSTSCRIPT Zachary and his parents no longer receive the help of the Family Advisory Service as he attends a school for blind children. His speech continues to improve at a steady rate.

5 Making Sense of the Child's World

The multiply handicapped child's entire life will be affected by the approach that people have to him and his needs. If he is seen as a child who needs to be protected against all danger and nurtured in a cocoon of sympathetic emotion, then he will behave as he is expected to behave: he will be handicapped; he will be limited; he will probably be under-functioning and withdrawn. If, however, he is seen as a child who, whatever his problems may be, is nevertheless capable of learning, then he will learn and grow and mature. No child is capable of doing or achieving more than he is physically or intellectually capable of, but all children are capable of under-functioning! It is the attitudes and reactions that people have towards him that will either limit or extend his achievements. Parents and teachers of multiply handicapped children need to view them as children with abilities. Their disabilities will affect the *way* they learn, but they *will* learn if given the opportunity—how much and how fast is difficult to forecast. It is immaterial how long it takes to achieve the task or goal, so long as it is attained eventually and provided that the child has had a lot of fun in the process.

The difficulties that the multi-handicapped child will face in making sense of his world are often of such enormity that it is only too easy to forget that he is a child, and not a robot to be programmed into fulfilling certain goals. Think of the child as a real child; put yourself in the child's place. It is easy to know that the child has multiple handicaps; it is far more difficult to remember and to take account of his normal needs in everyday situations. He will need far more awareness of things he can touch, smell and taste, and you will need to become more sensitive to his sensory input. Anything he can sense or experience for himself is important. Anything that he can be actively involved with will add to his knowledge of himself and how he can control his world. As he begins to grow in awareness, he will begin to develop a range of responses to his environment. If his experiences have been pleasurable and non-threatening, he will begin to co-ordinate some of his abilities. He may search to see what made a noise, he may turn towards your face, he may grasp his bottle or cup—because his experiences are becoming meaningful and he has learnt that the environment can provide him with pleasurable experiences.

We are often concerned that our children do not try to manipulate their environment through exploration. We have to remember that you cannot start to teach a child to manipulate the environment if he does not know what it consists of. His environment in the early years should be stable enough for him to appreciate that the objects he meets (such as furniture) will always be there for him to explore, and that the toys he is given will provide him with pleasure or occupation. If we concentrate only on his handicapping conditions and make his environment too different from that of the non-handicapped child, we can handicap him even more by his lack of knowledge of the normal environment. He must have normal experiences, for without these he grows up in a 'restricted handicapped' environment. The child without experience is the child without knowledge.

It is extremely important to bear in mind the newness to the child of all the objects with which he comes in contact. Because we are so concerned to show him the right way to use or manipulate something, we often presume far too much about his knowledge and do not give him time to explore and manipulate objects for himself before expecting him to use them correctly. For example, if we watch a non-handicapped child who is given a spoon for the first time, we notice that he will bang it on the table, turn it over, mouth it, look at his reflection in the bowl and use it in a variety of creative ways. Only after considerable experience of using a spoon to feed himself will he appreciate that this is an object which usually goes into his mouth and that it is not used for anything else. I feel that we should take time to observe non-handicapped children in their play so that we can provide the same sort of normal tactile experiences for the multi-sensory handicapped child.

There are many things you can do to help your child to develop this necessary exploratory experience. At first, you may have to help him co-actively to reach out to the things you provide, but eventually he will learn to explore by himself. He needs to be intrigued by toys so that he is encouraged to manipulate them for his own pleasure. A ring or rattle or string of large beads should delight him, as will any toy that makes a noise when hit or squeezed. Show your child that the toys are there and what they can do, and then leave him to explore these toys whenever he wants to. Change them occasionally, introducing toys with different sounds, colours or textures.

Safety Point. Please make sure all your child's toys are safe, non-toxic and too large to be swallowed. Toys that appear to be safe for a sighted hearing child are often extremely dangerous and pointless for the multiply handicapped or deaf-blind child.

— Toys should be small enough to examine but too large to swallow;
— should be non-toxic and non-breakable;
— should have no loose, broken, sharp or movable parts that could be swallowed or on which the child could damage himself.
— Examine the toy with your eyes closed. This will help you to appreciate what it is the child is learning to manipulate and whether or not he will get any real information from it.
— Be careful about naming toys until you have discovered the way the child uses them; you will often find that it is better to name the use to which the child can put the toy rather than the toy itself. For instance, think of three types of ball: one ball might produce a squeaky noise when it is pressed, one might be bounced when thrown and one

might wobble when it is thrown. If you name each one simply as 'the ball', you may miss its main other feature.

One of the most important areas in tactile work is to provide experiences that will lead on to self-feeding skills. If the child is never or only rarely allowed to play with messy substances, he will not have the kind of experience necessary to accept different textures in food and to eat them without difficulty. Very often multiply handicapped children are described as having feeding problems, but many of these may be unnecessary and may arise from having poor tactual experiences in the early years. If a child has had very poor or no experience with different textures, or if he is tactile defensive, no progress can be made in the area of self-feeding. We need to understand that the way the child plays is directly related to self-feeding skills. If he is able to put his hand into a container in order to pull out a toy; if he has awareness of his mouth and either mouths toys or puts his fingers in his mouth; if he is willing to explore or play with soft or hard objects; if he has the ability to hold objects using a tripod grip (using thumb and two fingers to hold)—then we can say that that child is ready to learn to feed himself. It is important to observe a child's play before embarking on a self-feeding programme, because it might be necessary to compensate by providing appropriate tactile experiences if he is to achieve self-feeding as naturally as possible.

As well as considering the child's previous tactile experiences, it is also important to look at his general interest in food. No one learns readily to self-feed if he actively dislikes the food that he is given. It is an interesting experiment to blindfold yourself and ask a friend to feed you without warning you what the food is going to be. You will notice that it is very difficult to identify many foods unless they are distinctively sweet, sour, spicy, hot or cold. Then apply the knowledge that you have gained from this experiment to the child for whom you are designing self-feeding activities. You may decide that it is more important to help the child actively to enjoy his food before he can learn to feed himself; you may decide to alter some of the tastes that you are giving him by making the food more interesting, perhaps by adding tomato ketchup or honey or beef extract. Many people comment that certain multiply handicapped children appear to enjoy food which would appear to be more suitable for adults, such as curries, Chinese meals or smoked fish and meats: clearly, if the child's other senses are impaired, he will tend to get much more enjoyment from more flavoursome foods rather than the bland food which is so often thought to be more appropriate for young children. If the child you are working with does not appear to enjoy food, it is well worth experimenting with flavours in drink as well as in food at mealtimes.

John, Sarah and Mary are three multiply handicapped children whose families have used the Family Advisory Service. Sarah presented at the time of referral as a child with a marked feeding problem. Suggestions to help her towards self-feeding are described later in this chapter. Mary and John were described to us as blind 'non-communicating' children who were both hard of hearing and who had each had long stays in hospital as a result of severe illnesses. It is self-evident that if a young sighted hearing child goes into hospital, he will suffer some form of disturbance through being parted from his primary care-giver for prolonged periods. A great deal of research and observation of young children in hospital has now ensured that, for the most part, they are nursed and handled by one or both parents, and many hospitals provide facilities for the child's parents to remain with him at the hospital during his stay. If we can expect the sighted hearing non-handicapped child to be disturbed by changes of routine, then no one should be surprised when the handicapped child resists all change and shows his anger, frustration or sorrow at being in a strange environment with people he does not know, who, for very good reason (such as injections), have to hurt him. It is small wonder that these children do not want to explore their environment.

Mary and John are not exceptional; it is quite usual for young children who are handicapped to have to go to unfamiliar settings such as clinics, hospitals, doctors' surgeries and other unknown places, for legitimate reasons. However, if the blind child does not hear well and the deaf child does not see well, and if the parents are unable to explain what is about to happen, then that child is bound to become fearful and show his fear in a variety of ways. Mary's activities emphasised the importance of understanding her environment and John's programme was written to help his parents to interpret the world to their child, who is unable to explore it for himself because he has an additional physical disability.

Many multiply handicapped children's problems are compounded by the multiplicity of their disabling conditions. A physically handicapped child may have, as well as difficulties in hearing and seeing, an extra disability in being unable to explore objects with his hands or fingers, and may have the additional burden of being unable to hold objects to explore them with his mouth. For the blind child, mouthing is often an essential part of his ability to appreciate the properties of objects. If children can touch the surface of an object but cannot 'look around' that object, they will have no idea about its size or dimensions. Mouthing increases understanding. If a child's physical disability is so severe as to prevent him from exploring his environment for himself, then he is further disabled and can be said to have an additional emotional and social handicap.

In order to help physically disabled children who also have sight and hearing problems it is vital to look at the child, to imagine yourself being the child, to enter into that child's life, in order to be able to formulate the type of activities he needs. It is extremely important to spend time on this observation period before thinking about the best ways to help him achieve his optimum capacity. For instance, people who do not really look at the child and his needs will provide a completely unsuitable learning environment and yet will have the highest possible motives.

Let us imagine a mythical child named Fred. He is aged four years, has spastic quadriplegia, is totally blind and hard of hearing.
Wrong
The wrong programme would give him exercises for his body,

auditory training for his hearing, and bring him a box of toys and pieces of material to explore and play with. It would not involve his parents and school in daily communications about his activities and would ensure that Fred would be confused and miserable for much of the time.

Right

The right programme would arise from careful observation of Fred's environment both at home and at school. It would take into account all his past experiences and would try to plan for his future needs. It would be based on the fact that Fred is a whole child who is unable to see and explore for himself; his programme would include explanations of what is going on around him, what is happening to him, what the other children are doing and why, and would always bear in mind that Fred cannot see for himself.

This is not as easy as it sounds. Many people who work with totally blind children remember that they are blind but forget that they cannot see! By this it is meant that blind children need to learn everything through non-visual methods. They have no means of knowing or interpreting what they are hearing unless they have a verbal explanation or are so close to the source of sound that they can recognise it for themselves. The blind child who is hard of hearing needs to *know* that he is listening to sounds that make sense to people around him. A 'bang' can mean the door has banged, the drum has banged, a car has back-fired, or something has dropped from the table. When we hear a 'bang', we have had enough visual information and enough past experiences to be able to interpret what we hear. Our children, because they do not have this visual information, need people to act as their guide through an otherwise chaotic noisy world. Nearly everything we see as adults has meaning for us. For a multiply handicapped young child, nothing will have meaning unless it has been thoroughly investigated, explored or explained. Our children need to be encouraged to *explore the possibilities* of the world around them.

So Fred's programme, if it is to be a good programme for him, will also provide him with the means of exploration.

He will never (or hardly ever) be left to sit for longer than a few minutes without someone interpreting his world. Fred's programme will include the knowledge that a physically handicapped child who is also blind and hard of hearing must always know where he is. When he sits on a chair, his feet will be on the floor. If he has to sit in a wheelchair, he will only use it for necessary periods and will not spend his life in it. When he is taken to the toilet, he will be told where he is going, why he is going and usually he will have been asked if he wishes to go there. In other words, even though he is a young child, he will be seen as a child who is normal in need.

Most four-year-old children, as their parents will report, are able to control their actions, are able to ask for and often demand certain activities, and their toys will have been chosen with their personalities and interests in mind. Fred does not want to play with a box containing meaningless toys and pieces of material. He needs activities to which he can relate and from which he can learn. Most multiply handicapped children find it difficult to play alone and will soon drift into the self-stimulatory activities discussed in Chapter 9 if they are not highly motivated. No child can actually play with more than one toy at once and very few children find any meaning in random pieces of material.

Fred's good programme will recognise that he needs to know about whole things before he can be asked to explore what so many people call the tactile box. He needs to know about his whole body and how his body parts connect with each other; for instance, he needs to know that his head is on his neck, where his shoulders are, that he has a back and a front, that he has two hands and two feet. He needs to know that with his two hands he is able to achieve more than with one hand, that having whole body experiences is not enough and is not an end in itself. He needs to know about other people, and that they have bodies, hands and faces, and he needs the opportunity to experience this. We meet many children who only have a very primitive notion of themselves and their surroundings and, in conversation, we discover that the child is never given the opportunities to learn that sighted hearing children are given all the time. Some of our children have never been out in the rain or the snow and have certainly never sat in a puddle or helped to build a snowman.

Anyone who wishes to devise a programme for a multiply handicapped child must start off with the deliberate intention of increasing that child's knowledge of himself and his environment so that, ultimately, like all other children, he will be in charge of making his own decisions. Fred's programme will therefore help him to learn to control his environment, so that he will be invited by all of his experiences to explore more and more for himself. Our lives are not limited in texture, colour or sound and neither should the lives of the multiply handicapped children with whom we work.

John

John is totally blind and hard of hearing. He is unable to stand but can sit up if propped up with cushions. He makes a few babbling sounds but it is clear that he does not hear perfectly. He is two years old and spent his first year in hospital as a result of a severe illness. He lives at home with his parents and older brother and has started to go to a local nursery for handicapped children.

Exploration programme recommended for John
As John had spent so much time in hospital he had no clear understanding about his environment, neither did he appear to understand what any environmental sound meant. We thought that he should be helped to understand where he was in his environment by alerting the adults in his life that he needed a clear mental map of it.

1   When John is taken from one part of the room to another, he must always be told where he is going.
2   When he is at home he obviously knows who is speaking to him, but, as a matter of course, all other people, particularly in the nursery, should 'announce' themselves before they move him by stating their name and telling him what they are about to do, like this:

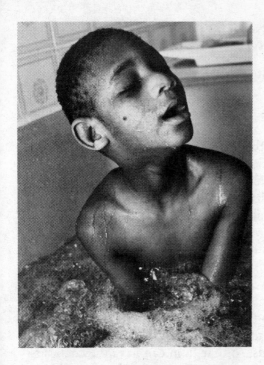

The deaf-blind child
needs to know as
much as possible
about his body in
different situations
. . .

. . . and that other people are different.

'John.' (Then he knows it is he who is being spoken to.)

'Hello, John, it's Mrs Brown. I'm going to pick you up from your chair and take you to the toilet.

'John, let's find the door.

'Let's find the door together. Here is the door. I'm going to open the door.

'Let's go through the door, John, and we'll walk down the hall to the toilet,' etc.

It is only by repeating in a clear but conversational way all the information which we pick up visually, that John will begin to make sense of his environment.

3   Listening to tapes and records can be fun, but John needs to have the opportunity to absorb the sounds around him. It is far better not to play the radio or have extraneous background sounds, so that John can have the chance to listen with an adult to the sounds that they hear together. A distinctive sound maker can be attached to the front door, so that the children know when the front door has been opened. Sound-making clues can often be of immense value to a young child with impaired vision.

4   John needs textured clues and 'body image' work if he is fully to interpret his world. Hardweave carpets, thick rugs and shag pile carpets all give children the opportunity to identify different areas of their house or school. Because it is very uncomfortable and gives very little information tactually, many children do not like plastic material to sit on. We prefer our children to sit as upright as they can with their feet (minus socks if possible) flat on the floor and with their hands free to play in front of them. When we move with our children from one area to another, those who can walk pick up a great deal of tactual information from different floor coverings. We recommend swimming as a 'whole body' tactile experience for all our children unless it is contra-indicated for health reasons.

5   People are the best toys for any young child, but particularly for John. It is fair to say that very few visually

handicapped children who are not mobile are able to learn effectively unless they are working in a one-to-one situation. (We recommended that ten minutes should be set aside as often as possible throughout the day for John to have a variety of one-to-one experiences with an adult. Sometimes these times would be for John to learn to activate a toy, sometimes they would be for singing sessions and nursery rhymes, sometimes they would be normal rough and tumble play, but, whatever the activity, it would be clear to the adult and John that these were to be his times for learning together.)

6 John needs to stand, sit and lie down as often as a child who has independent mobility. In other words, all of the adults working with John need to remember to change his position (with appropriate warning signals) as often as possible. All these changes of position must have meaning and purpose. (We advised his parents to think of John as though he had his own independent mobility. In this way they would give him the opportunity to change his position in as natural a way as possible. He would sit on the floor, in his chair or on the sofa to play; sometimes he would stand to play. He would move forwards, sideways and backwards for a purpose—to retrieve a toy or come to his father or mother.) As John does not have independent mobility or the ability to stand, opportunities for mobility would appear to be more limited, but in fact he can be provided with a standing frame to enable him to stand, a seat with a tray in front of it to enable him to play, and opportunities throughout the day to sit on the floor and the sofa.

7 John should always make journeys with a purpose—to the toilet, to the dining-room, to go out for a walk. He should always be informed as to the purpose of the journey.

Unlike some children John does not have a feeding problem, but he does have a difficulty in that he is unable to pick up a spoon or a cup for himself because of his physical disability. We therefore recommended that John's parents should contact their occupational therapist to obtain special spoons and cups which he could hold.

Sarah

Twenty-two-month-old Sarah has light perception and may prove to have some useful near vision. She is hard of hearing and no one is certain exactly what she understands. She has cerebral palsy and can now stand but is still learning to walk. She can use her hands, but if she does not want to touch an object or a toy she will pull her hands away immediately, which means that she rarely explores new things.

Touching activities recommended for Sarah

Sarah is very defensive about touching unfamiliar things and needs lots of opportunities to touch a whole range of different materials, particularly wet, sticky, messy substances (including food), we made the following recommendations.

1 Sarah should be encouraged to play with water, starting off with pure water and gradually adding things to it so that it gets thicker over a period of days or weeks. Her parents could try finger painting with a mixture that, to start with, is far more water than paint. As Sarah gets used to this, her parents could increase the amount of paint and decrease the amount of water.

2 Dry materials like rice, macaroni and dried peas are useful materials to explore. At first these could be put in a very fine fabric bag so that it doesn't feel quite so threatening. Although Sarah might dislike touching these at first, her parents could place some of her favourite objects in the mixture (on top of it at first, then half-buried, and totally buried as she gets used to the feel of it). Pasta comes in lots of different-sized pieces—the large coiled pieces of large macaroni are good to begin with, progressing to the finer pieces over a period of time.

3 Soft material could be used to place favourite objects on; it could then be wrapped around part of the object, and eventually the whole of the object could be covered. When Sarah is quite happy touching the material, her parents could help her to uncover the object.

4 Tactile experience includes warm and cold objects, such as food from the refrigerator or air blown on her hair from a

hair dryer. As Sarah is defensive about touching new textures, many of her first touching experiences can be with the rest of her body, e.g. hair dryer on hair, hand-held shower spray on her body and baby lotion on her legs and feet.

5 One of the most important areas of tactile play is finger play with food. (We thought that Sarah had rarely finger fed.) Sarah needs this kind of experience if she is to begin to accept different textures in her food and eat them without difficulty. Finger feeding is a stage she needs to go through if she is to eat properly in the future. At the moment she won't touch different textures, nor will she eat food of different textures, so any progress she makes in the one area is going to help progress in the other. Her bowl should be put in front of her so that she can put her hands in it if she wants to while her parents continue to spoon-feed her as usual; this way she will also get the chance to know her bowl and that there is food in it. She should be encouraged to place her food-covered hands to her mouth. She may do this fairly quickly or it may take time, in which case her parents could give her gentle encouragement to touch the food and taste it from her fingers. She may throw food to begin with. We are sure that Sarah's routines should be changed only in very small ways and very gradually, so that progressing to finger feeding will, from her point of view, be just another step in an enjoyable activity.

So many parents report that their children have 'feeding problems' that we find it useful to ask them to write down the food that they give their children in any one day. Often they are quite surprised at the quantity of food their child is managing to consume. Some parents may be so anxious for the child to 'feed' (perhaps because food has been associated with keeping him alive when he was a small, premature baby) that they will give him so much food that he is never hungry enough to self-feed at mealtimes. We have met extremely well-nourished children who have been reported as 'never eating a thing'. One mother, when we asked her to write down everything she gave to her rather large little girl who had totally refused to self-feed, discovered that she hand-fed her almost half a loaf of bread, three packets of crisps and three bananas, as well as a variety of soft puddings. Little wonder that her daughter had decided against self-feeding!

Mary

Mary is a totally blind baby aged 18 months, with a severe sensori-neural hearing loss. We feel that Mary needs to develop listening skills before she becomes mobile, so that when she can move freely in the environment she will have a greater awareness of the meaning of environmental sounds. She also needs to develop exploratory behaviour and tactile skills, so that when she meets objects or toys within her environment, she will be motivated to explore them for herself.

Listening and touching activities recommended for Mary's parents to use at home

It should be noted that all the activities that have been suggested are for a child who is sitting with an adult in close proximity. Sometimes it will be convenient for her parents to have her on their laps to show her how to achieve something; at other times they will be sitting near her.

Sounds. Mary's parents should feed back all her spontaneous sounds as soon as they are made; for example, if Mary says 'ooo', then they should repeat it back to her immediately. As often as possible they should try to help Mary become aware that communication through sound is a two-way process:

Mary makes the sound;
her parents repeat the sound;
Mary makes the sound again;
her parents repeat the sound again.

Over a period of time, Mary should come to realise that, just as her parents can imitate her, she, too, can imitate them. This is the beginning of knowing that communication is a two-way process. There is no such thing as a 'non-communicating' child, but sometimes children's messages may not be clearly understood. If Mary is encouraged early enough to realise that her parents understand her, that they are there when she 'speaks', we can, hopefully, eliminate the behaviour problems of the older multi-handicapped child who is unable to get his message across except through extreme means or who withdraws into repetitive behaviour.

The world for the totally blind child can be confusing enough without the additional burden of a hearing loss. Even a relatively minor hearing loss which would barely hinder the sighted child is of grave importance for the blind child. Mary's parents were therefore encouraged to understand that, for their child, all the sounds that she was able to hear had to be interpreted and that, because of her sensori-neural loss, she would not be aware of many of the sounds which they were hearing. They should show her where sounds were coming from within her normal environment. It is often not appreciated that even something as simple as a door opening, a bell ringing, a car passing by in the street, or even laughter, have absolutely no meaning to the totally blind child with a hearing loss. These sounds will need interpreting to Mary until she has either matured enough to be able to show that she has appreciated a variety of environmental sounds, or until she has enough language to be able to demonstrate that she knows what has caused the sounds she hears. As well as interpreting environmental sounds, Mary's parents were encouraged to play games with sound-making toys. The games we suggested were, wherever possible, a repetition of the two-way games which we have recommended to initiate imitation. Using a sound-making toy that is within Mary's range of hearing, her parents should first help her to explore and play with the toy and become familiar with its sound-making property. Once it has been established that Mary enjoys playing with the toy, they can then:

> use the toy to make its familiar sound;
> encourage Mary to reach out for the toy and then play with it;
> present the toy to Mary from different directions so that she becomes accustomed to searching for the sound maker;

try moving the toy slightly further away each time, so that Mary becomes accustomed to the idea of concentrated listening, directionality, reaching out and connecting the fact that sound-making toys bring their own reward.

Touching. In order to reinforce the need to familiarise Mary with searching for sound, we felt it was important for her to learn to search for dropped objects before she became mobile. She was already beginning to scan an area of her mother's lap if she had dropped an object which was a favourite of hers. We felt we could extend this skill and help her to practise by invariably helping her to search and scan with her hand until she found favourite objects on her mother's lap. We felt that it was always important to name everything with which Mary was playing, but that the name should be appropriate to her understanding and experience. For example, a bell could also be called a ringing toy, a ball could also be called a throwing or catching toy, a jack-in-the-box could also be called a toy with a lid. A child with vision very quickly comes to realise that certain toys and objects have distinct properties peculiar to each, and that it is acceptable or unacceptable to behave with them in certain ways. For instance, it is acceptable to throw or catch a ball; it is not acceptable to throw a jack-in-the-box. It is realistic to try to ring a bell; it is not realistic to try to ring the cat! A blind child with good hearing would very soon get the message through experiment and trial and error, as would a sighted deaf child. The deaf-blind child, on the other hand, will often need guidance for much longer, and more help from his parents and teachers in playing with his toys, because his hearing does not tell him about what his eyes cannot see.

Cause and effect toys such as musical boxes are often given to multiply handicapped children to play with, because it is felt that it is important for them to learn to manipulate them. If the cause and effect toy is to be helpful and aid the child's learning process, then care needs to be taken to ensure that the child is physically able to manipulate the toy and has the ability to hear it, or the visual capacity to appreciate its action, otherwise he or she will remain unrewarded after a great deal of effort.

When recommending Mary's parents to use cause and effect toys, we helped them to choose toys within her capabilities and her hearing range. We demonstrated that, with some toys, Mary would get extra stimulation from the *vibration* of a musical box or radio, but that this stimulation was secondary to her needs. Cause and effect toys are very useful when helping a child to learn to use two hands during activities. Some of our children need to be reminded that they have two hands and sometimes showing them how to put both hands around a cup will help them to get better control of their hands. If they enjoy eating, then being encouraged to use both hands during mealtimes, one to hold the bowl and one to hold the spoon, will sometimes help them to learn that they have got two useful tools (hands) that will help them to control and manipulate their own environment.

6 Motor Skills

Judith Peters, our physiotherapist, writes:

Helping a young child to learn to move and want to explore his environment because it seems a good and exciting place, must be an enjoyable experience for both child and parent. This cannot be over-emphasised. Parents, teachers and physiotherapists unite under the umbrella title of 'developmental therapists' whose aim is to work as a team through the medium of structured play in co-operation and with mutual exchange of ideas, in order to help the child achieve his own potential. In our sensory impaired children it is well to remind ourselves that movement occurs in response to sensory input to the body. Sensory messages are received via the muscle/joint receptors, and this is an area often overlooked: if you close your eyes, lift your arm up to shoulder level and try to bend your elbow to a right angle, you are able to do it accurately because every tiniest tension within your muscles and tendons is relayed to your brain. A child must experience movement and the feel of varying positions to learn about his body and how to move with smooth co-ordination.

It is vital accurately to assess a child's stage of development. The equivalent stage may not be attained simultaneously in areas of motor, language and social achievement, and it can be confusing to know a child's chronological age while observing motor development that may only be at the level of a tiny baby. However, if this is the level at which the child functions, he must build from this stage, for to miss out the foundation stones of development would only lead to insecure body control.

At birth babies exhibit reflex asymmetrical, jerky movements. As the nervous system matures the movements become smoother, symmetrical and purposeful. Head balance and a degree of trunk control precede the ability to sit. Being able to put arms out to save oneself from falling must develop before standing or walking can be achieved. At the earliest stage, symmetry and experience of a variety of positions is encouraged. Prone (tummy) lying is of particular importance for stimulating head control and stability of the shoulder girdle. Side lying is vital to help the hands come together, where they are able to explore in midline. Head turning leads on to the beginnings of rolling, which is the great trunk strengthening activity. As the trunk and neck muscles come under control and strengthen, the scene is set for gaining sitting balance. This may need to be helped by the support of a suitable chair—frequently required by children with hearing and visual impairment. The very experience of the upright posture stimulates increased muscle power and places eyes and ears in an optimum position for receiving signals. Learning to support the body continues, needing much practice and encouragement until, as the rising-to-stand reactions appear, the child is able to explore the standing posture.

As with the problems of attainment of sitting, the visually impaired child may be unmotivated to pull himself to a standing position. I often use the 'fun' experience of being stood up (with support) as a stimulus for the child himself to want to 'have a go'. The pressures occurring within muscles, joints, and on the soles of the feet when we stand, are quite different from those we experience while lying down. These stretches and pressures—or proprioceptive sensations—are in themselves a stimulus to maintain standing. For this reason I frequently place a child in a standing frame and ask teacher colleagues to think up a really enjoyable activity for the child while the standing session is in progress. The standing experience, like every other part of therapy, must be a happy occasion.

Many of the children I see have either muscles that are too tense (hypertonic or spastic) or muscles that are lacking normal tension (hypotonic or floppy). Understanding the reason for these variations in tone and the special ways of handling the children are important areas for all members of the developmental therapy team to understand. Special footwear may be needed and, certainly, watching for correct foot and leg positioning during play, sleep, carrying, feeding and dressing is essential.

Finally, physical development takes time and maturity. The ladder towards full motor control is similar for all children, but for some the speed at which the rungs are climbed may be slower. Progress will be faster at some times than others and the plateau periods can seem long. If on some days you have less time to work at therapy, or there are moments when you, or your child, feel less inclined to work, remember that an 'off' day may well be a pause ready for a spurt forwards at another time.

We must appreciate that all multiply handicapped children differ radically one from another, and that they are each absolutely unique. The combined sight and hearing problems of these children (which may be further compounded by physical disabilities) make the ordering of their chaotic world difficult for parents and professionals alike, but once appropriate individual programmes have been devised the children can usually be led on to achieving the same developmental sequences as their sighted/hearing and able-bodied peers.

All our relationships with the multiply handicapped child will be built on a sense of touch, and often the child will need whole body cues (things which impinge on his body) in order to participate fully in the things we offer to him to play with. Very few young blind children are motivated to move forwards and they may have little or no knowledge of what their hands can do. In order to help the children with whom we are working to achieve good movement, and hence mobility, we have to encourage them through whole body movement to become aware of their own bodies in space, and we may need to pattern their movements for them. Children who have impaired sight and hearing always need to collect information about their environment using touch, so the use of touch must be developed to help compensate for the lack of visual and auditory input.

In this chapter we shall look at some of the ways in which touch can be used to help to establish trusting relationships and encourage the children to explore their environment. Touch is an important tool for learning and an invaluable teaching technique that can add an extra dimension of meaning to a potentially confusing world.

The deaf-blind child learns best when he is in close physical contact with an adult; initially, it may be the only means by which he *can* learn. Touching (with someone else co-actively, see p. 132), is a vital step in developing a trusting relationship and, for some children, may be the beginning of communication. The multiply handicapped child who has his difficulties compounded by reduced sight and hearing will need the additional information provided by your body moving alongside his. Most relationships are built on touch and whole body cues, and this is only possible when the child has learnt to trust the adult and is secure in the relationship. Once he realises that the adult is useful to him, he will allow himself to be drawn into experiences, *hand on hands*, so developing his ability to interpret the messages he is receiving through his body.

Since young blind children are unable to model themselves on adults, it is often important to show them how to undertake an action. From behind, the adult can guide the child to use both his hands in a purposeful way while maintaining close physical contact. A multiply handicapped child does not automatically reach out to his environment and may need to be physically directed to the most effective ways of gathering information. As the child begins to master a skill the amount of physical direction can gradually be reduced.

Often a multiply handicapped child dislikes the experience

of touching new things. It is important, however, to encourage him and to find ways in which new experiences can be made gradually more acceptable, for unless he is adventurous in this way, he will never be motivated to explore his environment. He may need the adult to help him to move out into space and will often need to use touch to extend his area of knowledge.

Many multiply handicapped children use different body parts in order to gather information and build up a picture of a new room, and tactile signals should be provided within the room in order to encourage further exploration. Initially the adult will need to bridge the gap between the child and his surroundings, this support being withdrawn as he gains confidence in mastering the skill of exploration. Although many deaf-blind children have useful residual vision, they will still need to use touch to reinforce the visual images they are

Learning to explore his own environment.

receiving. They will need to explore the objects they discover in the room, to pick them up and mouth them or finger them, just as the sighted child would explore them visually. This is the kind of sensitivity that needs to be encouraged and given time to develop. Some children, as well as using their fingers and mouths, will use their heads to explore the objects they find in the room. Usually this exploratory behaviour is valid, but we have to guard against it developing into a mannerism that will distract them from exploring further. All our children need more time to gather information to discover the whole of the room rather than parts of it. Without an interest in touch, the child may have unnecessary aversions that could hinder learning and will certainly hinder his ability to move about in a strange environment.

Intensive play is often used to help children form a warm, trusting relationship with an adult. We join the child in his activity and, indeed, reproduce his activity with him, responding to the pattern that he has established. No child learns in isolation, and one of the most important aspects of helping him to learn that the environment is something to explore is first to encourage him to move around with an adult with whom he feels secure. Before embarking on intensive play, which will involve the adult in being aware of the child's patterns and natural rhythms, we have to do four things:

1 We must *know the child* and know what skills we wish to achieve with him.
2 We must *identify the abilities* that we feel he should be encouraged to master.
3 We need to *look at the child's difficulties* and try to alleviate some of them within the intensive play activities.
4 We need to *observe the child*, to ascertain what special qualities he will enjoy within an intensive play situation. If he is a very quiet child he will probably not enjoy loud drumming; if, however, he is extremely active, he may respond to certain rhythms and songs.

What we are trying to do is give him both body awareness of himself and awareness of us as people who are prepared to reciprocate his body movements; he will then be drawn to-wards us and be willing to learn from us. Many deaf-blind children have a very poor body image, and one of the aims of an intensive play session is to give them an awareness of, in particular, where their hands, head, feet, arms and legs are, and the different ways there are of moving their bodies. This activity is at first reciprocal and shared and will then lead to the child imitating other movements which the adult wishes him to attain. Very few multiply handicapped children will imitate an adult unless they have gone through this prior activity of reciprocal and shared activity through intensive play.

Often it is possible to give the children balancing activities to help them manoeuvre their heads and bodies into different positions and to give them the feeling of freedom of movement. Music and strong rhythms will, of course, help in the intensive play session, as well as songs that echo and reciprocate the natural movements the child is showing. Songs about the child rocking, smiling, moving, shaking hands, moving backwards and forwards, can all be incorporated in an intensive play session.

It has to be remembered that the aim of working in this way is for the child to learn to trust the adult. Once this trust has been established, he will usually allow himself to be moved up or down in space, to reach out, to move his hands and body into different positions. Once he realises that moving in space is an enjoyable experience, he begins to order his world; he gains a clearer picture of his body and can then be shown ways of moving forward.

Intensive play is a means of helping the child to gain the confidence to move his body, limbs and hands in space through interacting with an adult. Once he has gained confidence he will need the necessary motivation to move his body forward in the environment, and he needs to know that the objects he locates within the environment have meaning. He may need extra training to help him to absorb information and to recognise that he can manipulate toys and other objects.

Gross Motor Skills

Motor skills are essential for furthering any activity or skill area. Without movement he will be unable to explore the world, to sign or speak, to take individual steps; and he will not move without the incentive to do so. It is quite normal for us to see a blind child still lying passively at the age of a year, when his sighted peers will be beginning to crawl forward. If the blind child is deaf or hard of hearing or has physical disabilities, then his incentive to move will be further reduced. It is therefore extremely important to ensure that he is encouraged to sit at the same time as his sighted and hearing peers. This can be achieved quite simply by propping him up and, with the advice of a physiotherapist or occupational therapist, obtaining a chair that will give him support, so that he can experience the upright position at the right developmental age.

Many blind children do not crawl, and this should be seen as normal motor behaviour. They may instead progress by rolling, squirming or bottom-shuffling. Once the child has learnt to stand and walk forward, he may feel safe enough and have a good enough mental map of his environment to start to crawl. When a blind child crawls, he is in danger of banging his head on the furniture, so he will often prefer to bottom-shuffle. I have witnessed blind children walking backwards rather than forwards, so that they hurt their bottoms rather than their heads when they move around. Again, we feel it is quite normal for the multiply handicapped child to stand and hold on to furniture or to cruise around holding on for much longer than his sighted hearing peers. When learning to move up stairs, we feel that it is very important that the deaf-blind child should be enabled to go on all fours for much longer than the non-handicapped child, because he needs to feel and appreciate the depth and height of the stairs before being encouraged to stand and hold on to the banister rail.

Many multiply handicapped children are able to explore a familiar room with no problems, but some of our children who have additional physical handicaps are unable to do this unless they are helped, co-actively, to move around the room. Some may be affected by cerebral palsy which is usually the result of brain injury in early life. There are three forms of cerebral palsy. The child with spasticity has disordered control of movement and may appear to be quite stiff, often needing intensive physiotherapy. Another form of cerebral palsy is athetosis, which causes frequent involuntary movements that interfere with the normal movements of the whole body. Ataxia is the third type, and this usually causes the child to have an unsteady gait or difficulty in balance. Some children with cerebral palsy may have difficulties of perception and may have their problems compounded by a distorted sense of touch, so that they are unable to distinguish the important features of objects with any clarity.

If the child with cerebral palsy is also deaf as well as blind, clearly his mobility and ability to move around and explore his environment will be extremely limited unless he is given a great deal of consistent and careful help. A co-ordinated effort will have to be made to ensure that he has the same opportunities for exploration as his more mobile peers. He will need his environment structuring so that he is given every opportunity to understand where he is at all times. So often we see physically handicapped children sitting in a wheelchair and then being wheeled, with no explanation, from one part of the room to another, taken to the cloakroom and toileted, or taken into the playground, without heed to the fact that these children need more explanation, not less, if they are going to be able to play their part, fully, in the life of the school. If we were able to govern the way we behave to our children by always 'putting ourselves in their place', we would ensure that people always spoke to us clearly, that they always explained where we were and what we were about to do. We would certainly try to ensure that we knew in which room we were sitting. Many of the children whom we see are seated on chairs that are either too small for them or too large, so that their feet are in the wrong position. Blind children *must* know where they are in space, and if their feet are not on the floor they will be denied this important information.

Within the classroom and in the home environment, children, if at all possible, should be able to have shoes and socks off, because they can gain much valuable tactual information from their feet. Wherever possible, the child should have his position changed as often as his more mobile peers. When playing, he should sometimes stand, sometimes sit and sometimes lie on the floor. He should not need to sit in a wheelchair all day. The deaf-blind multiply handicapped child needs help to explore a room and, if he feels safe and secure, he will do so with confidence, although he will, of course, need constant supervision to protect him from danger. We encourage our children to go swimming unless it is contra-indicated for health reasons. Most of our children can be helped towards greater mobility through circuit training, which can best be described as an enjoyable way of moving to achieve a certain goal. It always starts with a definite signal and stops using another signal. This signal can be provided by using an object such as a chair, bench or stool, or it can be by using a certain activity such as throwing a ball, lying on a large physiotherapy ball or bouncing a ball; or the signal can be signed and said: 'Stand up and play,' 'Stand up and walk,' or 'Sit down, we have finished.' All circuits can use a variety of skills and activities, but they are so structured as to provide the maximum amount of mobility training accompanied by a sense of fun and

Reaching for an object.

achievement in a task completed. A circuit for a physically handicapped child might begin with a start signal, and then the child would be helped to move from the exercise mat to a physiotherapy ball, and from there to a vibrating cushion which would be used as the rewarding motivation for his achievement. A circuit for an active able-bodied child might start from sitting at a chair, and then the child would be asked to complete a circuit designed to help him to move more carefully from one place to another; his circuit might involve careful movement along a bench, stepping from there through the rungs of a ladder placed on the floor towards the goal of a trampoline, a favoured activity and the child's ultimate reward.

Fine Motor Skills

Just as gross motor activities ultimately help the child to bring order into his world by giving him more mobility and movement, so fine motor activities help him to become as independent as possible. Without good fine motor skills, the child will be unable to self-feed, dress himself or achieve other social skills with any degree of competence. We need constantly to watch the child's hands and the actions he is able to make with them, so that we can assess the next stages he needs to achieve in order to attain full competence. For example:
   —How does he hold objects?
   —How does he transfer objects?
   —What movements does he make with his hands?

Feeding Skills

Feeding skills are inextricably linked to other skill areas which include postural control, and fine motor and perceptual abilities relating to touch and vision. As well as the fine motor skills which are important in thinking about self-feeding, we need to ensure that the child's posture is correct so that he will feel comfortable. He should have his feet supported and his ankles, knees and hips should be bent at right angles. Only if a child is sitting comfortably and confidently is he able to give his full

How does he hold objects?

How does he transfer objects?

attention to feeding. The dish needs to be well within his reach and, of course, within his field of vision.

Once the child is sitting with his trunk well supported and his arms free to feed himself, he should be guided, with both his hands in the right position. The sequence of skills involved in self-feeding is common to all children, but those with a dual sensory impairment will develop at a different pace and the steps will usually need to be taught. Probably a child's first experience of spoon-feeding is having the food put in his mouth by an adult. Usually the non-handicapped child will be expected to participate quite quickly in spoon-feeding, but this may be delayed in the multiply handicapped child for a variety of reasons, one being that the child will not have the correct hand function to be able to participate fully and will need extra adult guidance. The adult goes behind the child and is then in a position to hold his hand over the spoon and guide it from the plate to the mouth. The child may also need assistance in filling the spoon or in conveying the loaded spoon to the mouth. As soon as it is obvious that he is able to manage without physical prompting, this should be withdrawn gradually, from hand over hand to hand over wrist to hand over elbow, until it is not needed at all.

Often a multiply handicapped child's ability to self-feed is related to his ability in tactile experiences and in other fine motor perceptual areas. If he is unable to pick up small objects from a container and transfer them, it is highly unlikely that he will become completely independent in feeding until this skill has been achieved. If we analyse the skills necessary to feed, we see that we have to pick up the food or the spoon from a container, and then we have to lift that food to our mouths. (Note that I have not said that food is always conveyed to the mouth by spoon or fork because, with blind children, it is often necessary and important for them to finger-feed for longer than the sighted child. If the blind child misses out this stage then it is unlikely that complete self-feeding will be achieved.) We would generally say that it is the act of taking an object out of a container and conveying it to the mouth that is the important part of learning the skill of feeding.

Fine finger movements are inextricably linked with other skill areas. No activity can take place without movement. When considering the child's ability to communicate we have to consider his hand function and his motor co-ordination, because he will be unable to sign successfully unless he is able to make the quite fine hand movements. It may be useful to look at the child's fine motor skills using a checklist to note how the child uses his hands and fingers and recording this in an objective way.

Having recorded these abilities, it is then possible for parents and teachers to plan activities that will help the child to achieve the next goal. (It should be noted that some blind children will not build towers of cubes but that the same skill can be used in putting beads on an abacus.) No skill should be seen in isolation—postural control and locomotion will take place at the same time as the ability to use fine motor skills. Any vision the child has will modify or expand his ability to use fine finger movements.

Zoë, Bill, Colin, Robert, Holly and Gillian are all children who needed different types of activity to help them achieve fine motor and large motor skills.

Zoë
Zoë is a deaf-blind child. She has light perception and her vision is not likely to improve; she is profoundly deaf and is unable to hear anything other than an extremely loud noise, when she is wearing hearing aids. She has a chromosomal abnormality, which means that she has very floppy muscles and is unable to stand alone unsupported. Zoë enjoys using her hands to explore things; we would say that she is tactually aware of her surroundings.

Motor activities recommended for Zoë's parents to use at home
We have always felt that Zoë's tactile awareness is at least average for her age. Her tactual memory and use of her hands thoroughly to explore the object she is given show a very good degree of co-ordination. As she is a truly deaf-blind child who

is impeded by her lack of mobility, we feel that we should use her good tactile skills to help her to achieve mobility. We recommend the following:

1 To put Zoë on a large bouncy ball and, having let her explore it with her hands, encourage her to move from side to side and drop forward to give her the feeling of moving, balancing and saving herself.

2 To put Zoë over her parents' legs onto her tummy, with her arms forward on the floor, so that she will learn to use her arms and legs as a possible means of movement and, while she is on her tummy, to help her (co-actively) to stretch forward in order to reach a vibrating toy.

3 To move her arms and legs rhythmically, to roll her vigorously from side to side, back to side, front to side, waiting for body signals to restart the movement.

4 To help Zoë to be aware of her feet and legs, in the same way as she is aware of her hands and arms, by tapping, tickling, pushing, banging, stroking and squeezing them. Many children get a great deal of information from their feet; they also need to know that their feet are 'there' and are potential playthings.

5 Zoë's feet should be flat on the floor in front of a correct-size table. She should gradually move upwards so that she gets the feeling of rising to standing to play at the table. Once she appears secure in this position, she should be helped to move down from standing to sitting. She needs to know her 'edges'. (At the moment we feel that she knows that she has hands but not that she has feet, that she has arms but not that she has legs, that she has a back which she enjoys lying on but not that she has a front.) We therefore feel that it is extremely important to spend some time each day in practising moving up and down, moving side to side, moving to search and getting pleasure from the act of movement.

6 As Zoë enjoys playing with toys, can reach for them and search for them, we feel that she should be encouraged to increase these skills. Her parents are therefore asked to:

a) Give her a bag with an unusual texture. This special bag would only be used for a searching activity. One or two favourite toys would be put inside it and she would be helped co-actively to feel in the bag and retrieve the toys. We feel that Zoë would soon learn to search tactually for these favourite toys.

b) Help Zoë to place things deliberately, otherwise once out of reach they have simply disappeared as she can neither see nor hear that they still exist. She should be encouraged to put things down and then pick them up from the same place, and then to put things into a box or other container and pick them out. She needs to discriminate between when a thing is there, when it is there but out of reach, and when it has gone. If she was encouraged to put things down with a slight bang, which would make the table or the box vibrate very slightly, she would be aware of their position. When an object such as her cup is removed, she should always feel it go and then have the BSL sign for 'gone' signed with her co-actively.

c) Large and small toys and everyday objects should be brought very slowly from one side of Zoë to her middle, so that she begins to realise that objects can be moved and are constant in shape. At the moment she is used to playing with toys that are in front of her, or reaching for her cup and spoon in front of her. What she needs to learn is that she should expect objects to 'appear' from any angle.

Bill

Bill is 18 months old. He has cortical blindness and cortical deafness and we are not yet certain how much he can understand. He is beginning to roll and wriggle to move some distance. He helps to pull up to sitting from the supine position, and saving reactions forwards and sideways are developing when he is sitting. He is able to get into a modified 'prone kneel' position, with weight taken on his hands and forearms. He shows signs of rising reactions—helping to pull up to the standing position. Bill tends to hold his arms in a bent position. He will extend his arms and through them is able to stand with a little encouragement.

Suggestions for Bill

Bill is now ready to learn much more about the sitting and standing positions. He should spend much of his time upright so that his muscle tone and postural control will improve. He should stop using a baby rocking chair and progress to a small seat that gives a little support in the vertical position; for example, a Rifton toddler chair.

Bill should stand with support and should try a Joncare Flexistand to encourage his upright posture. He should use it briefly, initially for perhaps five to ten minutes, and it is important that he enjoys the experience. We feel a fun activity could be introduced during the standing session.

Bill should be encouraged to bring his hands together in midline—this is sometimes easier when he is lying on his side or when he is sitting in his chair.

He should be encouraged to reach and extend his arms. If he withdraws his hands it may be easier to push his arms gently into the extended position from just above and behind his elbows.

Bill needs to roll, and by pulling up under his hips he should be able to get into prone kneeling with arms fully straight. His shoulders should be pushed down gently and firmly to encourage him to push against the floor. (Gaiters may be useful to assist this.)

He needs to move from lying to sitting by pulling him up obliquely, letting him do as much of the movement as possible.

Use of his postural muscles can be encouraged by tilting him forwards and sideways when he is on an adult's lap or on the floor. His hands should learn to protect him and save him from falling over.

Colin

Colin is 22 months old. He has very limited vision and a severe hearing loss. He has very floppy muscles and at the moment will not tolerate having his body moved in any position; he is only happy when he is lying with his back on the floor, consequently he resists all new experiences.

We felt that it was vital for Colin to experience a variety of positions, but that he must enjoy them; otherwise he would react adversely to being asked to sit up and later stand.

Programme for Colin
Colin must experience a variety of positions. Try to encourage prone (face down) position by using it for some of his dressing or bath preparation, so that he comes to expect to be on his tummy as part of the process.

Holding Colin under his tummy in the air stimulates head and leg extension and can be great fun if accompanied by rhythmic singing games.

Stack soft blocks and encourage him to reach to knock them over from lying. Put them just at the limit of his reach. Encourage him to continue the game in the sitting position (emphasis should be on the activity of blocks falling and *not* on the new sitting position!).

Bouncing games on an adult's knee may stimulate pushing with his feet (we recommend that Colin should have his socks off for this activity as he will gain more information from his feet).

'See-saw' tilt games on an adult's knee to encourage saving reactions: forwards and sideways especially (backwards develops last). Support him at the hips rather than with hands on chest, but he may still need the higher support at the moment.

A large therapy ball can be used for tilt and saving games **but** only if Colin finds this enjoyable and not frightening. Try this slowly at first and work towards extending the activity later on.

Sit Colin in the bath, on a rubber mat to anchor him, and with water only up to his hips so that he does not topple over. Put him on his tummy in the bath. Support him under the chin so that he is not frightened by a sudden dunking. (Of course later on one encourages face into the water and bubble blowing, but only when Colin is ready.)

This whole programme should be **fun**—we have to present the activities we want to encourage so that Colin will enjoy them and not resist them as at present.

Robert

Robert is two years old. He is totally blind and hard of hearing. He has excellent mobility skills for a blind boy of his age. He loves movement, and revels in rough-and-tumble play. This confidence is expressed in his walking, where his gait is smooth and well-balanced, and he shows few of the gait adaptations characteristic of a blind child. He enjoys exploring and manages to avoid colliding with head-high obstacles. If he is given an environment encouraging free and purposeful movement with plenty of physical play, his movement skills should continue to develop.

His fine motor skills are also progressing well. He is happy to explore new objects by touch, and co-ordinates his two hands in constructive exploration. He will need guidance to be shown how to distinguish the distinctive tactile characteristics of objects, when a formal programme of concept development and teaching is started.

A major reason why Robert's skills are so well developed is that he has been trained to use his hearing well for mobility tasks. He can hear a quiet sound-making object producing either high or lower frequency, and locate it extremely accurately if motivated to do so. He is alert to sound in the environment, and will 'still' himself to concentrate when any new sound is apparent. He responds both to aeroplane sounds (less than 500 Hz) and to a crisp packet or dummy rattle, when involved with another activity. He recognises his own name, and the tone of voice used by his family when communicating with him. He is not yet responding with words, and he is in need of an intensive language programme. His active curiosity with objects in the world, coupled with his interest in sounds, makes him ready to associate word with object. Robert can vocalise. Every effort is being made to increase his range of sounds through close one-to-one work, in that he appears to be a child with marked communication difficulties, yet able to use vocalisations to echo-locate.

Like many young blind children, Robert has not learnt simple techniques for finding his way. However, he does not need them at present, since he is able to re-discover distinctive locations in a room by use of sound clues. While he is still so keen to explore he will not learn formal techniques, since he is happy to discover new things all the time. In a consistent room layout, where furniture and landmarks remain reasonably constant, he should learn the basics of room orientation. This would be particularly helped by the location of *one* discreet constant sound clue, such as a ticking clock or a humming fridge.

Suggestions for Robert

1 Robert is ready to learn directional concepts such as up/down and in/out, which can be introduced through action play with his own body. He should learn the names for the different parts of his body in a one-to-one situation.

2 A consistent effort to name every object he comes across, and every sound he hears, should be made. He has not learnt the value of language and is ready to do so. His actions need to be described and his environment explained to him in a clear, concise way.

3 He needs a range of action games, encouraging him to continue exploring as wide a variety of movements as possible. He loves jumping and bouncing. Show him how to roll, jump from foot to foot, climb frames, swing, swim. The more movements he is shown now, the more confidently he will move in the future.

4 Auditory awareness. Sound games that include clear rhythms, distinct pitches and imitation work should help him to discover that communication is a two-way process. He already enjoys toys that make a variety of noises. Try extending this enjoyment by, for instance, rolling between you a ball which rattles.

5 Robert cannot see so, whenever possible, he needs to be told about the sounds he is hearing and all environmental

sounds should be identified for him so as to give him more necessary information.

6   It might be useful to think about identifying certain situations that occur every day, using a set phrase. Examples of these are: going to the toilet, getting dressed, getting washed, eating food, going out for a walk; Robert will then learn that words can be presented in phrase or sentence form. His name should always be put first in any phrase, so that he knows that the sentence applies to himself. Examples:

'Robert, now you are going to put on your *coat* and go out for a *walk.*'

'Robert put on your *bib* and eat your *dinner.*'

The words in italics are those we would expect him to recognise in context first.

Holly

Holly is aged three years. She has rubella syndrome, is profoundly deaf and had cataracts removed at an early age. She is an alert, very affectionate little girl. She has good head control and quite good general muscle tone. She rolls actively as a means of locomotion and also crawls. She climbs from kneeling to standing, using her mother or furniture for support. She cruises round the furniture and with help will walk a few steps. When supported at the hips, she stands straight with feet plantagrade (flat on the floor), but as yet she has underdeveloped arches and foot musculature. She does not like to sit but has the ability to do so. She tends to lean back for support, but when sitting on an adult's knee shows developed saving reactions.

Her fine motor function is well developed—she has a good pincer grasp of a dried pea with the left hand and excellent grasp with the right. Her left hand is often held flexed, with the arm medially rotated, and occasional movements have an athetoid writhing character. She is tactile defensive, retracting her shoulders and withdrawing her hands from her environment.

Suggestions for Holly

1 Holly should be supported from in front for walking by her hips, elbows or upper arms. Many young visually handicapped children will walk forward *to* an adult and to an attractive object, but unfortunately sometimes they are held from behind, which means that they are straining to hear what the adult is saying to them and tilting backwards in order to see or touch the person whom they are with. We would usually recommend that the child should be held from in front and not from behind when walking.

2 Holly should have her shoes and socks off as often as possible, and when it is warm she should have her clothes removed, so that she can gain as much tactual experience and proprioceptive information as possible.

3 Holly does not like to sit, so she should be encouraged to take up this posture before starting a game she enjoys. All movement activities need to be presented in such a way that she will enjoy them. She needs to allow herself to be tilted so that she learns to shift her weight from one position to another. Again, this activity can be presented as a game on her parents' knees.

4 Holly needs to reach and cruise further around the room, so her parents should place her toys at a slightly higher level (so long as they are within her range of vision). Reaching forward with two hands can be encouraged by pushing a ball to a parent. This activity should take place with the adult in front of Holly rather than to the side.

5 Large motor activities can often be encouraged on a trampoline or through swimming, unless either of these is contra-indicated for any reason.

Gillian

Gillian is aged five. She has a profound hearing loss and extremely limited vision; she is totally blind in the right eye and has tunnel vision in the left eye. She sometimes walks on tip-toe, but generally her motor development is very good. Like so many of our children, we feel that Gillian can be encouraged to improve her motor development by the use of a circuit, where it is necessary for her to complete a series of set tasks which enable her to practise certain skills.

Circuit suggested for Gillian

It is important for Gillian to learn that there is a definite start and finish to the activity. We usually use a chair for the start of a circuit and a favourite activity as the final reward—in Gillian's case this is a trampoline.

Fine motor activities suggested for Gillian

Gillian needs a great variety of activities not only to consolidate her fine motor skills, but in some cases to encourage 'skipped' stages of development in this area. She needs to learn to place rather than drop objects onto the table and then into a shallow container. She should also be encouraged to use her thumb for pressing, especially when some strength is needed —cause and effect toys such as a Jack-in-the-box, or turning on a torch, would be excellent. She could also gain strength in her fingers as a whole by rolling, pounding, squeezing and pulling at play-doh.

At this stage of development, it would be normal to see a child able to thread beads using both hands. However, with Gillian's tunnel vision, she will find this a very difficult task. It would be interesting to see whether she can screw a lid onto a jar and off again, if a reward such as a chocolate button was actually *in* the jar. It might just prove to be the necessary motivation. From this activity she could then graduate to using one hand to hold something and the other hand to turn, stir or crank an object; for example, holding a bowl with one hand and stirring with the other. Once this is mastered she should then be able to cut paper with scissors, and then use her hands separately to perform such skilled activities as playing a xylophone or drumming with alternating hand movements.

Self-Help Skills

The multiply handicapped child will be more likely to achieve self-help skills successfully if we see these skills as movements to be completed. The child needs to understand that all movement is for a purpose and that most of the movements he

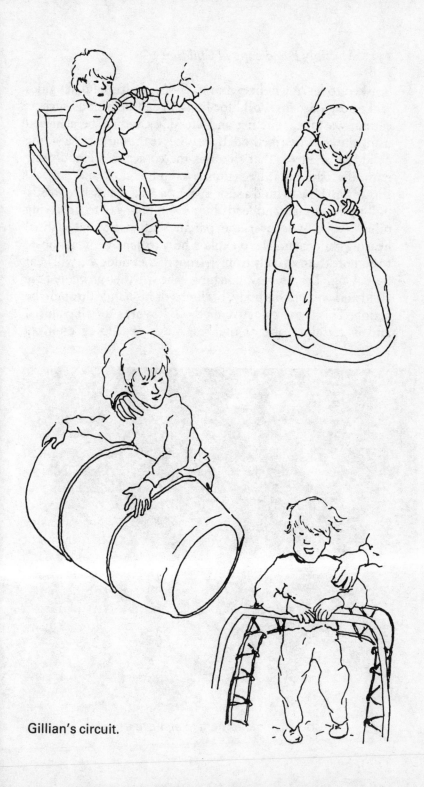

Gillian's circuit.

is asked to learn will help him to choose purposeful activities and to organise his world for himself. Self-help skills such as eating, washing, toileting and dressing can best be achieved using the co-active method. If we observe the parent of a young child, we shall see that she uses the co-active method quite naturally: she puts her hands over the child's and actively shows him how to hold a spoon, put on a shoe, brush his teeth, pull up his pants, and leads him on in this way to achieving other skills. Whenever the parent with a normal sighted hearing child is unable to explain how to achieve an action or to demonstrate visually from in front of the child, you will hear her saying, 'Let me show you how.' She will then go *behind* the child and will put his body, his limbs or his hands through the action. This is the co-active method. It works for all children and is certainly one of the best ways of helping multiply

Co-active movement to achieve a goal.

handicapped children to learn to perform most tasks, particularly where their impaired hearing and vision does not allow for verbal explanation. All daily self-help activities can be accomplished by teaching them co-actively through as individual an approach as possible, which bears in mind the child's needs. The child's programme should be designed to fit him; we should never expect any child to adapt his difficulties to our programmes!

7 Communication

The absence or presence of what adults call language can completely alter their perception of a child. In this chapter I hope to show that there is no such thing as a non-communicating child and that all children, however severely handicapped they may appear to be, are in fact trying to communicate and are making their own attempts to obtain information. It is only because these attempts to communicate are not always understood that children are sometimes deemed to be non-communicating.

Very often children whose early attempts to communicate have not been noticed may develop bizarre behaviour mannerisms, which are discussed in detail in Chapter 9. The difficulty has been that the child has not learnt that he can make things happen, that he can manipulate the environment, that he can learn to tell people that he needs—for example, to eat, to drink, to play, to go to the toilet, and that he wants to do things. Because people have been unable to understand his attempts at communication, his world has become so chaotic that he has had to do the only thing possible, that is, commune with himself. Very often we have met children who have had visual training—that is, helping the child to look in order to absorb information, to recognise objects and to choose and organise toys and activities for themselves. We have also met children who have had auditory training—that is, helping the child to learn to listen, so that he can understand some of the sounds that he is capable of hearing and can recognise what they mean; and we have also met children who have been 'taught to sign', with the idea that they can learn to make things happen, that they can learn to manipulate the environment. Such children have been taught 'useful' signs such as 'eat', 'drink', 'toilet', 'sit down', 'stand up'. When we have met these children, their parents or care-givers have been surprised that the child has *not wanted* to use the signs; we have had to point out that *signing* is not in itself communication. Communication is a two-way activity; it is inter-action.

The normal child without a sight and hearing loss and with normal experience, soon learns that he can manipulate his environment by smiling at his mother and father, and he will make eager welcoming movements as they come near him. He practises the sounds that he can hear, and they are delighted as soon as he makes an approximation to sounds that they want to hear—'mum-mum', 'dad-dad', 'gan-gan'—and interpret these to him; by their delighted behaviour the sounds that he makes are reinforced and soon become recognisable as 'speech'. The more the child makes sounds and the more they are reinforced back to him through caring adults, the more he will 'speak'. By the age of 12 months it is quite clear that a lot of children understand many simple instructions and, by the age of 18 months, they are often able to recognise and use more than 20 words. The path they have used in learning speech has been that their behaviour has been reinforced, that what they have at first used in a reflex way has been received and rewarded by an adult with whom they are used to interacting. They have usually been in a one-to-one ratio when they have learnt speech.

Exactly the same process applies to the deaf-blind or multiply handicapped child. What he often does not have is the adult's perception of his early attempts to communicate. If people have not noticed that he has been attempting to communicate and have therefore not interacted with him and reinforced his behaviour, this early attempt to communicate is lost. When a child has early individual interaction with an understanding adult, he will begin to expect things to happen. He will be far more interactive, far more demanding and will try to make the adult understand him, will feel that people are aware of him. We need to change our approach in order to enter the world of the deaf-blind or multiply handicapped child; we need to approach them as normal children are approached by their caring parents.

No two children develop in the same way or at the same speed, but generally speaking, we can say that all children follow the same sequence of development if they have normal sight and hearing. It is self-evident that the multiply handicapped or deaf-blind child is unable to use his distance senses of vision and hearing to receive non-distorted information. In Chapter 5 we discussed the various means for helping the multiply handicapped or deaf-blind child to integrate sensory input from his damaged distance senses and to increase input from his other senses, and everything that is said or recommended in this chapter must be assumed to be taking place alongside those other vital programmes. Communication touches on all aspects of development and cannot be separated from them.

The young normal sighted hearing child quickly builds a basic feeling of 'security'. He soon understands that all his near senses, the senses of smell, touch and taste, have meaning for him because he receives information about them from his distance senses. He will welcome kissing, cuddling and rocking, will welcome the smell and taste of different foods, and will be curious about what the world is going to bring him next. These early experiences are often denied the deaf-blind child, for he has no means of receiving the same information. The stimuli that impinge upon him are often extremely frightening, for he has no warning that things are about to happen and so is unable to formulate a relationship between himself and his surrounding world. The multiply handicapped child whose distance senses are seriously impaired has little information on which to build his world image. He is unable to organise the various sense impressions he receives. He therefore fails to discover any structure to it. Often this means that his near senses—taste, smell and touch—may also be subject to distortion for, because of the lack of warning, he may have guarded his body from being approached. The child has been unable to understand any of the messages which his parents or other adults have been trying to send him, and he has therefore had to retreat from the world. The focus of his behaviour will have been his own body.

Early child/adult relationships depend to a large extent on impinging on the child's body. It is the basis for a great deal of his learning. If the deaf-blind or multiply handicapped child has lacked early interaction with an adult, we have to try to provide this through *intensive play* activities. We have to give him another message about his body and about his place within the world. The normally developing child has a natural predisposition towards wanting to understand how his actions will affect the world and the people that he meets within his world. The adult, quite instinctively, will capitalise on these interests. The same applies to our interactions and communications with the young deaf-blind child; we are attempting to enter his world in a non-threatening way. As with the normal child, we want to join him in his movement, help him to understand through our actions that we are accepting him and that his movements are acknowledged by us. So we often join the child in his patterns of movement within the intensive play situation. The idea of intensive play, as discussed on p. 113, is that we are using movements familiar to the child which may help him to realise that he is initiating interactions with us. There will be many opportunities for such interaction throughout the day and we must seize them all.

Again, if we look at the normal child, in the first six months of life he has extremely close interaction with one other person for most of the time. We must find opportunities for this one-to-one interaction with our young deaf-blind or multiply handicapped children. All learning at this stage is through close physical contact. If we look at the normal child with his mother or father we see their pleasure in rocking or swaying or rolling their child. If the adult who is working with the multiply handicapped child does not receive the same pleasure, then she will convey to the child that early body interaction is 'boring'. We must be as open and as full of fun as a mother and father with their child. By participating in the child's movements, we help him to understand that we accept him, that he has a reference point for his activities, that it is much more fun to join someone else in a rocking activity than to do this alone. Rocking can lead to side-swaying, to being moved backwards, to reaching upwards and outwards, and to changing an otherwise chaotic child's absorption with self-stimulation.

Through intensive play activities, it is hoped to establish that the child's own body is giving good messages, that these messages are received by the adult and that they will be modified or extended according to the child's needs. The child will become involved in the interaction and may begin to anticipate and restart a movement following a pause; he may give some indication during the session, which the adult can interpret as a signal to re-start the activity. The child may indicate in a variety of ways that he has enjoyed an activity, perhaps by moving his limbs, or bouncing his bottom, or pushing the adult, or taking the adult's hands and putting them back in the correct position for the movement to be re-started. It is important that this stage is recognised and that the child is encouraged through the adult's response to use movements to effect change.

Within this intensive play the adult should be alert and ready for any attempts by the child to signal a change in the activity or to communicate. She should sometimes pause to provide an opportunity for the child to communicate his feelings and needs, and should be ready for the child to indicate that he wishes to continue or stop an activity. Again, we look back at the normal child with his mother and father. They would never continue an activity if the child showed distress; they would continue if the child showed through his actions that he was enjoying the interaction. We are providers of information to the child and, if we are not prepared to receive the information about his feelings, then we cannot expect him to want to communicate with us through other more formal means.

We must always examine ourselves and our behaviour when we are looking at what is called a 'non-communicating' child. Have we observed his behaviour? Have we responded to his responses? Have we looked at him as a source of information? Have we given him a constant picture or a distorted, incomplete picture about ourselves? Have we provided a basis for security so that he knows what is about to happen next within the intensive play situation? Have we given a routine and an order to the intensive play? Consistency within the intensive play situation is the key to further development. The patterns of the actions which we provide should always be able to be anticipated by the child. We should establish rituals that the child can understand and messages we know he is willing to receive. We should aim to help him understand that we are willing to receive his messages.

How different this is from the child who is just expected to receive messages in the form of signs, which are basically commands and which he is supposed to follow. We need to establish a loving, trusting, one-to-one relationship with the child; we must help him to understand that he has an identity and that we have a different identity. We need to show him that there is some particular quality that makes him unique, separate from other people. Each child will have something special, of real meaning to him, which we can find to help him know that he is himself; this could be an activity or a routine that he enjoys. Within this intensive play activity he begins to expect the adult to communicate with him through his body and each will provide modifications of the original movement. The main aspect and the most important element of intensive play is the fact that the child is interacting with an adult who is alert to his signals and body messages and responsive to him and his rhythms, just like the mother and father of a non-handicapped child.

Only when the child has shown that he understands that the adult is capable of receiving his messages should we lead him towards imitation, which at first will be established through use of *co-active movements*. Very few deaf-blind children have the ability to understand signs which they can visualise only briefly; most will need all new signs introducing co-actively. (An explanation of co-active movement is given on p. 132 and line drawings are shown in Chapter 2.) Co-active movement occurs when the child follows the adult's movements, using his hands to touch and monitor the adult's action. It can only occur if the child is willing to have physical contact with the adult, which is why intensive play activities are so important. In order to learn to sign, the child needs to learn to imitate, and he needs to know that it is worthwhile to imitate the adult's hand movements. Learning signs that are basically for the teacher's needs, so that she can impose commands on him —such as 'wait', 'stop', 'go'—are of very little use to the child and he will have little incentive to reproduce them. He will have every incentive, however, to reproduce signs which allow him to manipulate and order his environment, so the first signs are usually 'play', 'eat', 'drink', 'jump'. We shall call these signs *activity signs* and the other signs *command signs*. The child's ability to focus on activity signs, which represent and depict the actions of others and which he has an incentive to learn because they are fun for him to use, will have far more chance of succeeding than the command signs.

Intensive play leads the child towards being able to form personal relationships with a caring adult. The co-active method of working leads him to interact with his environment and to imitate. Until he has passed through both of these stages he will not have learnt that he has the means to manipulate other people. Once he has learnt this, then what is sometimes called 'signing' can commence.

Before the child is ready to learn a formal structured signing system, he must have built up a warm and trusting emotional bond through intensive play activities and co-active participation. These bonds do not develop accidentally or immediately and need to be planned for by the parent and the teacher. If the child does not have this warm bond with his parents and adults, then they may all become discouraged and will not be able to make the effort to continue. The cycle of interaction with the child requires much time, effort and sensitivity, and we shall need to observe the child carefully before we decide at which stage to start. We know only by observation where the starting point should be. There are three fields of observation:

—observation of normal child development;

—observation of the child;

—observation of the adult who is undertaking the interaction.

Observing the child within the normal developmental sequences and seeing what he is already achieving, should lead us to an awareness of what he needs help in interpreting and how we can help him to communicate his needs to us. Once we have done this, we are in the position of deciding whether or not we will use a formal signing system with him. Situations must always be provided that will stimulate him to interact with the environment—particularly with the adults whom he meets—to help him to solve problems and to help him establish a dialogue at the appropriate level.

A programme of communication through signs for any deaf-blind or multiply handicapped child will need to cover his entire waking hours. It is pointless for the school or the home to use any system without the co-operation and awareness of the other people involved. Again, if we look at the normal child, communication does not stem from his parents *or* his teachers exclusively. He is communicated with on different levels by a variety people all the time he is awake. All the people he meets, casually, formally or informally, are giving him experiences of communication. This must also happen with the deaf-blind child. Only very slow progress will occur if he receives communication from a restricted number of people and at restricted times throughout the day. All the people involved in his life must be prepared to learn means of communication that he can perceive, so that he can respond meaningfully at all times to his environment. Unless his learning is based on global experiences, it can become one-sided and meaningless. The over-riding principle must be that he, in his attempts to communicate with us, must recognise that we are capable of understanding his messages.

It would be extremely easy (and foolish) to categorise all deaf-blind children and treat them in exactly the same way; their situation is unique and presents a unique problem for those who care for them, but we must never lose sight of the fact that they are also unique as individuals (not just as deaf-blind individuals) with their own unique place in society to which they can bring their own talents and abilities. All too often they are seen as severely handicapped persons who have

The child and adult need to establish a warm bond between them . . .

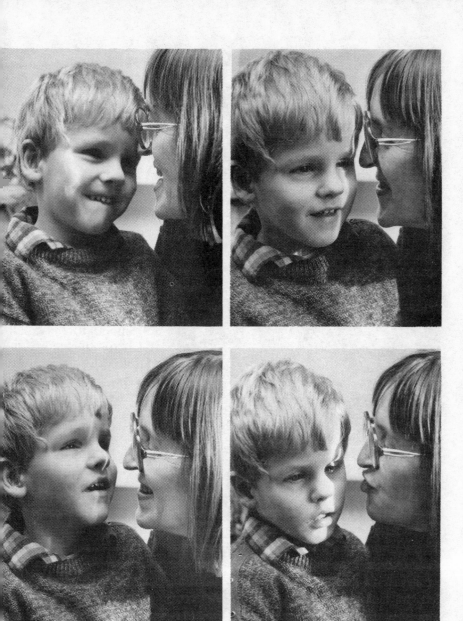

at first the adult will respond to the child's attempts to communicate (informally) . . .

... and then the child can be expected to start to respond to the adult communication (formally).

enormous communication problems, and the enormity of these problems can confuse us as to the best way to alleviate their isolation.

Before deciding to adopt a signing system to help a deaf-blind child to understand and be understood, we need to examine which children would benefit from particular methods. We would use signs for any child unable to participate in two-way oral communication, because we feel that by using signs to support the spoken word we can help the child to interpret the information he is being given in a more meaningful (and pleasurable) way. We might use signing with a blind child with a hearing loss or a communication disorder, and have often found that by signing with these blind children they have started to babble and then speak. We have not found that signing restricts the use of speech.

Method

The first necessity is to provide a structure to the child's learning environment. By providing a *structure* we can produce *anticipation*, the first crucial stage in producing a situation where two-way communication can happen. This can be achieved by repeating a series of movements prior to events that are significant to the child. All children are able to receive and draw some understanding from a complex image, well before they are able to express one. To this end, it is necessary to initiate a system of providing tactile signals for all the actions which the child is able to recognise, and signs for the different objects and stimuli which he will encounter.

It is important to bear in mind that I am talking about substituting a tactile information system for a visual and hearing one. If the child could see and hear, he would appreciate the constancy of his environment and would understand a great deal of what he heard. I feel we should take our lead from the 'normal' world in which the child lives and always remember that the children we are working with are *normal children who are deaf-blind* and that they live in the normal world. I want as many people as possible to be able to participate in two-way communication, so a signing system which most people can understand is vital. I also bear in mind that I do not want to ask our children to learn a series of signs and then 'unlearn' them, either because they move to another school or district, or because they are no longer appropriate for the child to use. I feel that deaf-blind children who are going to use signs should use those adopted by the deaf community—British Sign Language—and that only this signing system is appropriate.

1   Any 'eccentric' individual sign which the child has can be 'shaped' into a British Sign Language sign over a period of time.
2   Any gesture which the child uses can be formed into a standardised British Sign Language sign.
3   The child is part of the community and is, effectively, a part of the signing 'deaf' community. (I want our children to participate in community life and to be understood by as many people as possible.)
4   Eccentric (invented) signs which are only known by a few people do not really serve our children's needs; indeed their use could make them even more isolated, as few people will know these signs, and their efforts to communicate may be restricted even further.
5   I see real dangers in using any system other than British Sign Language, as the child's opportunity to interact with others would be very severely limited and his vocabulary would be confined to signs taught only by 'teacher'.
6   I have experimented with most of the British Sign Language signs taught to our children and can vouch for the fact that all signs have a quite distinct tactual and/or spatial element which can be learnt and understood by even a very young child.
7   British Sign Language can often be understood by non-signing members of the community, giving the child more chance to communicate with others.
8   If a limited, specially formulated, highly individual signing system is invented for a particular child (and I have seen children who have used such systems), that child is:

—limited to those signs only;
—always isolated from the other children until he learns their signs;
—further restricted by the highly specialised nature of the signing system—other people may not feel they are capable of using these signs.

British Sign Language is a legitimate language. Staff, parents and indeed, brothers and sisters, are more likely to carry out a consistent signing system if they are using signs which they also see being used by other staff, parents and children. British Sign Language is a 'natural' language and as such is constantly growing, therefore the child's vocabulary can be enriched and increased as the need arises.

Communicating Environment

When we introduce language to a child, we do not restrict our speech to that which he understands. We certainly simplify, and we place emphasis on important words, but we—and all teachers—recognise the need to provide a communicating environment from which the child learns to draw information about individual objects and meaning or information about the whole process of social interaction. If we use a restricted 'invented' sign systems, we treat our children totally differently from the way we treat them in other situations. We *expect* them to follow the normal stages of development as far as they are able, and we should expect to interact and communicate with them in the same way. For a deaf-blind child, the need for two-way communication should never be seen as just the province of the language specialist; it is the necessary province of anyone wishing to be with the child and, as such, must have as its key a readily available system to which the majority of people will have easy access.

All children are capable of communicating. We may be able to assist them to be understood and to understand by introducing the use of systematic and structured British Sign Language, so providing each child with the maximum possible interaction with the community.

Babbling

Before a non-handicapped child learns to speak, he invariably babbles. We should expect the same sort of behaviour with the deaf-blind or multiply handicapped child but, if he has been learning signs, what we should expect is an increase in his hand movements. Often the child who has been newly introduced to signs will start to 'babble' with his fingers and you will notice what at first appear to be random hand movements. In fact these are often the first signs that the child is beginning to be more aware of his hands and fingers, and is an interesting state for the alert adult to be watchful for. Any approximation to signing should be accepted. Just as the normal child has his babbling reinforced by the attentive parent repeating his sounds back to him and accepting any attempt to say a new word, so should the deaf-blind child have his behaviour reinforced by parent and professional alike.

Sometimes we are asked to recommend signs to use with a child first. Again, if we look at the normal child's development, we see that no parent would ask a teacher what words to say to their sighted hearing child, and we apply the same principle to the deaf-blind child. Clearly, the first words for any child must be words that he is interested in learning. (It is amusing to note here a list of words which have been suggested to us as appropriate for a young deaf-blind child to learn: 'please, toilet, hearing aid, good morning, more, finished, glasses, stop, sit down, drink, bath, plate, school, eat, wash, spoon, come, thank you, wait, next'; and to note the list of words which we recommended the child should be encouraged to use: 'play, eat, more, ball, walk, jump, I, want, yes, put on, take off, Mummy, Daddy, love, good, up'.) The first signs that are introduced to the child must have meaning for him. No child can be expected to want to learn 'command signs', although, of course, he will have to understand what they mean. It is not accidental that most children learn to sign 'biscuit' or 'sweet' well before they learn to sign 'sit down' or 'sleep'! We often recommend that parents and professionals, when beginning to sign with a child, should actually start with whole phrases, because we speak in whole phrases and not in isolated words.

'I want to play', 'Take off my coat', 'Love Mummy', 'Put on my coat and jump', 'Daddy swing me now', are all normal phrases which the young speaking child would be expected to use, and we see no reason why the young deaf-blind child should not be encouraged to use the same phrases.

The main difference between teaching a deaf-blind child and a deaf-sighted child is that, with the deaf-sighted child, signing is always additional to speech and is presented in front of him, whereas with the deaf-blind child the sign is quite deliberately introduced to him, co-actively, from behind. The reason for this is, that because the deaf-blind child is unable to utilise lip-reading, he may have to use signing as his main means of communication, so it is vital that he learns *how to sign*. (It is important to state here that we would never sign with a child without speaking to him, but that from the child's point of view all speech will be supported by the use of signs.)

If the deaf-blind child is very young and able to sit on an adult's knee, it is possible to manipulate his arms and hands through the signing positions; as he grows older the parent or teacher will go behind him when he is seated on his chair to show him the signs. Co-active signing can be described as another means towards independence for the young multiply handicapped child and as another means towards helping him to manipulate his environment. We have to be aware of hand function, the ability to interact with other people and the opportunities for communicating through signs which the child will receive throughout the day. Some British Sign Language signs which can be introduced co-actively to the multiply handicapped child are:

eat	pat one hand onto mouth
drink	put imaginary cup to mouth
ball	make two-handed outline of a ball
walk	walk two fingers along outstretched palm
jump	jump two fingers up and down on outstretched palm
I	point index finger onto chest
bath/wash	make washing movement onto body

put on	pull imaginary coat onto the shoulders using two hands
take off	take off imaginary coat from the shoulders using two hands
Mummy	tap first three fingers twice on outstretched opposite palm
Daddy	tap first two fingers on top of first two fingers
love	hugging movement
good	thumbs up
stop	two outstretched hands palms down in a quick downward movement
want	open right hand stroked downwards onto left side of chest

It will be necessary to sign with the child co-actively until he demonstrates by his behaviour that he can use the sign in context or that he can initiate an activity through his signing behaviour.

Many multiply handicapped children do not have a clear sense of their own identity and they may constantly need to have their names reinforced. Some parents and teachers decide to finger-spell or use an initial letter to identify themselves and the child if he is profoundly deaf. Where there is useful residual hearing, every opportunity should be taken to identify objects and the environment. Blind children with a mild hearing loss or who are language delayed, and hearing impaired children who have additional sight problems, have the need for identification and understanding about the people, objects and places with which they come into contact.

They Need to Know Names

It is important to remember that whereas we know the names of almost everything we see and hear, most deaf-blind children or multiply handicapped young children do not. We must have this knowledge at the forefront of our minds all the time for, if we forget, the child will never know who he is, where he is, who is with him, what he is holding, what he is doing, or why he is expected to do it. Naming and identifying for the child's

sake is an enormous responsibility and must never be forgotten. Unlike the hearing blind child or the sighted deaf child, the
multiply handicapped child will have to be given far more time
to process the information he has been given. He will require
more time to listen, look and feel, more time to absorb
information, more time to process that information, more time
to practise skills presented and more time to consolidate. If this
is true of the mobile deaf-blind child, it is even truer of the
profoundly handicapped child whom we see so often in
schools for children with severe learning difficulties. These
children usually require one-to-one attention throughout the
day if they are to maximise their potential, because they have
physical problems that also have to be overcome. They will
need even more input than the mobile deaf-blind child.

Putting yourself in the child's place will always ensure that
you will be able to keep to the following principles or guidelines:
—name yourself when meeting a child; do not presume he
knows you unless he can speak or sign your name immediately he sees or hears you;
—then say hello and spend time in greeting each other;
—then do the activity with the child, using appropriate
language/naming all the time;
—then remember to say goodbye;
—then remind the child when you expect to see him again.

*Keep to a routine which you know the child will appreciate
and from which he will learn*
Routines need not be rigid, in fact they are always better if they
are fun, but they will help the child to identify where he is in
space if you always adhere to these guidelines:
—say your name
—say hello
—say where you are
—say why you are there
—give good mapping/orientation clues which are constant, so
that the child can return to the same place on another
occasion

—give good orientation clues so that the child can one day find his way to the spot.

Clues should always be constant:

    a door is constant

    a cupboard can move

    a window is constant

    a chair can move

    a path is constant

    a tree can be cut down

    toys can move

    chairs can move

    desks can move

Unless you are absolutely certain that you intend the toys, desks and chairs always to be in the same spot for the rest of the child's time in the house or classroom, you have to be very wary indeed before using any of these as orientation clues or landmarks.

The behaviour of the child and his response to tactile British Sign Language should dictate to us whether or not we continue signing or whether we gradually fade it away. Many blind, hard of hearing children who have been introduced to signs, once they have learnt that the environmental sounds which they hear are meaningful and that other people have been able to understand their responses, have begun to communicate verbally. A very useful checklist on communicative abilities is contained in the Midwest Regional Centre for Services to Deaf-Blind Children's *Manual for the Assessment of a Deaf-Blind Multiply Handicapped Child*:

Spontaneous Nonverbal Communication

1   Cries and/or smiles

2   Smiles, vocalises, moves in anticipation or other display of expectation of familiar or pleasurable activity

3   Ceases activity in response to introduction of new activity

4   Pushes adult's hand away when wants to retain object, or as reaction to unpleasant thing

5   Places adult hand on object and pushes

6 Hands object to adult and waits expectantly
7 Leads adult to what child wants when it is in close proximity
8 Anticipates on basis of physical situation; definite participating action (Example: at juice time child will go to table without being sent)
9 Child leads adult to what child wants in another room.

Imitation
Body Movements
1 Resists being manipulated through body movements
2 Allows self to be manipulated through body movement; does not imitate
3 Moves alongside another person while being manipulated through correct movements (e.g., stand, sit, creep, scoot)
4 Moves alongside another person in imitation, but needs help in assuming correct starting position
5 Assumes correct starting position by imitating adult position
6 Imitates motor movement from adult model
7 Imitates sequential movements by following adult through them, one at a time (e.g. scoot, then crawl)
8 Imitates sequential movements after the adult has completed the entire series.

Limb Movements
1 Does not imitate limb movements
2 Imitates bilateral symmetrical limb movements (e.g. arms out or legs up)
3 Imitates unilateral limb movements (e.g. left arm up or right leg out)
4 Imitates bilateral symmetrical limb movements which are outside of visual field (e.g. hands on shoulders, hands on head)
5 Imitates bilateral asymmetric movement (e.g. left arm up and right arm out)

6   Imitates limb positions of a doll or puppet
7   Imitates limb movements of a doll or puppet
8   Imitates limb positions of stick figure drawings.

Fine Hand and Finger Movements
1   Does not imitate fine hand movements
2   Imitates hand clap
3   Imitates pat-a-cake and finger plays
4   Imitates 'pointing' (fore finger)
5   Imitates making two fists, and spreading fingers
6   Imitates simple hand gestures (bye bye, peek-a-boo, crude 'eat' sign)
7   Imitates asymmetric hand positions (one hand open and the other fisted)
8   Imitates holding out same number of fingers
9   Imitates pictures of finger positions.

Tactile Communication (Contact Communication, Tactile Cue, etc.)
Tactile command or message in this context means a gesture or sign performed upon the *body*. Not to be confused with gesture or fingerspelling in the palm. For example, tapping the child's shoulders as a sign for 'sit down', manipulating the child through the sign for 'go'.

Reception
1   Responds to no receptive tactile symbols
2   Responds appropriately to one consistent tactile message (e.g. knows teacher's hand on child's mouth means 'eat')
3   Discriminates between 5–10 tactile messages (one-word commands)
4   Discriminates between 10–20 one-word commands
5   Responds appropriately when given two sequential commands (e.g. sit and eat)
6   Responds appropriately when given three or more sequential commands.

Expression
1   Uses no tactile symbols expressively

2 Uses one tactile symbol appropriately, with a situational cue present (e.g. child gestures 'eat' only when child knows food is present)
3 Can discriminate between a few tactile symbols and use them appropriately, with situational cues present
4 Uses one tactile symbol without situational cues
5 Uses less than five tactile symbols appropriately, with situational cues
6 Uses more than five tactile symbols on own body to express self
7 Uses more than five tactile symbols on the bodies of other people to express self.

Gesturing (Pre-signing)

Reception

1 Understands no gestures
2 Responds to one gesture appropriately and consistently
3 Discriminates between about five gestures
4 Discriminates between about ten simple pointed commands or natural gestures (i.e. 'put it there', 'come', 'sit down', etc.)
5 Responds appropriately when given two sequential gestured commands.

Expression

1 Uses no interpretable gestures
2 Uses one gesture with situational cue (e.g. sees cup, gives 'juice' gesture)
3 Uses about five gestures appropriately with situational cues present
4 Uses one gesture without situational cues
5 Uses about five gestures without situational cues
6 Pantomines and creates own gestures.

No checklist is anything other than a checklist: a tool for teachers and parents to use to assist them in the further development of the child. One aspect which is very rarely part of any checklist is the adult's ability to interact with the child.

We need to be aware, when using any checklist on communication, that our attitudes, involvement and interest in the child will influence the communicative behaviour that he shows towards us. It is self-evident that if we are interested in the individual expressiveness of the child he, in his turn, will be receptive towards our attempts to communicate with him. If all he receives from the adult are short one-word commands —'sit', 'wait', 'stop'—then we should expect to receive the same type of staccato interchanges from him. The aim should be to create a fluidity of exchanges between the two participants: this is communication.

It is important to bear in mind that there are differing, legitimate means of communication: they all depend on interaction between two people and on the giving and receiving of information. Information can be given as a 'command' —'You are going to sleep now'—and the answer can be a statement—'No, I am not'—or it can be in the form of a question—Where is my biscuit?' and answer, 'In the cupboard'. Any communication between two people should be clear enough for both to be aware of what the subject of the conversation is about; both should be able to identify and recognise the subject and should be able to comprehend the interchange, and the conversation should be of interest to both parties.

Language competence takes up to three years to attain in the normal sighted hearing child. We should not be surprised if it takes longer to achieve in the child with multiple handicaps. The mobile sighted hearing child has an inbuilt incentive to communicate and a range of activities and choices to make, but above all the willingness of an adult to respond to his attempts to communicate. His parents have waited for his first word and have encouraged him by babbling, trying to gain his attention and showing by their delighted behaviour that they are willing to receive his first 'words'. Applying what we know about normal child development we should behave in exactly the same way with the multiply handicapped child, building up trust and confidence, and showing him that we are ready to receive his messages.

Messages

When we are giving messages to the multiply handicapped child, we have to be quite clear that we know *what the message is*. The deaf-partially sighted child and the blind-hard of hearing child each has a distorted image of the world, which we must remember in all our interactions with him. Zachary's mother tells the following story. Zachary was invited to go on a sailing holiday. For weeks before the holiday Zachary and his parents talked about the sea, which he had visited on several occasions, and discussed the fact that the boat would sail on the water over the sea. A great deal of preparation and discussion went into the sailing holiday so that Zachary would have a clear idea of what sailing meant. During the first ten minutes on the boat, which he explored with his mother, Zachary felt a large rope coiled on the boat's deck, and as soon as he felt it he turned to his mother and said, 'Can I get up now?' 'Up where?' asked his mother. 'Up on the swing,' replied Zachary. He had been well prepared for his sailing holiday, but no one had thought to give him the message that you only find swings in parks or gardens and not on board sailing boats.

As Zachary can now speak, he is able to convey to his parents if they have given confusing messages or if their message has not been clear. The majority of children whom the Family Advisory Service works with are profoundly deaf, partially sighted or severely visually handicapped. These children, unlike Zachary, will be unable to convey to the adults with whom they come into contact, that they are being given confusing messages.

Examples of Confusing Messages
—When trying to explain to a partially hearing blind child that he was wearing pyjamas, the teacher working with him patted his middle and said, 'Pyjamas,' and then asked, 'what are these?' and patted his middle again. The blind-hard of hearing child replied, 'My tummy'.
—At mealtimes, one mother was seen to be continually cleaning her child's fingers while at the same time saying and signing, 'Good food, food is good, eat your food . . .' But

was the message that was being conveyed 'don't touch, food is bad, food is sticky'?

If the messages which we are giving the child are confused, we should expect to receive confused messages from him. We have to ask ourselves what message we are putting in, what information we think we are conveying to the child, and then stand back and observe not only the child as the receiver of a message, but also ourselves as the giver of the message. By observing his behaviour and by responding to his responses, and by seeing the child as the source of our information, we can see what he is missing. Is the information distorted or incomplete? Have we provided a constant picture for him? Has he been given enough opportunities for reinforcement and understanding of the messages which we think we have been conveying? Does the child trust us enough to know that we will respond to his attempts at communication?

8 Structuring the Child's Day for Learning and Play

All children start learning from the moment they are born, but this learning process may be modified by the attitudes people have towards them, by a child's concept of himself, his abilities and limitations. Most parents of non-handicapped children expect them to achieve certain goals and will structure their child's ability to learn, quite naturally and unconsciously, by the things they provide for him to play with and the activities they enjoy together. The perception of their child's learning is largely governed by their own experiences as children and by their views of the child-rearing process, as taught to them by their parents, relatives and friends. Some parents may attend child-rearing classes and read books about child development, and the majority feel confident of their abilities to provide for their child's needs.

The handicapped child has the same developmental needs as a non-handicapped child, but the parents' perception of these needs may be altered by the importance that people have given to his disabilities. Parents may be advised that their child must receive physiotherapy, auditory training, visual training, etc., and may be so concerned about the specialist help he is receiving that they compartmentalise the child and label his needs.

When planning for the child's day we must remember that he is a 'whole child'. He may also have handicapping conditions, but his social, emotional and developmental needs are the same as those of his non-handicapped brothers and sisters. We need to look at the child within the guidelines provided for normal development and help him to achieve normal developmental sequences as naturally as possible. The multiply handi-capped child may need slightly different experiences from those of the non-handicapped child, to help him get from one milestone to another, and sometimes his route may diverge slightly, but he follows the same general pathway. He can usually be helped to achieve most of the same social and motor skills as his non-handicapped peers.

The new-born baby moves his hands in a random fashion and then, as the months pass, he develops the ability to grasp consciously and deliberately for an object held within his range of vision. This process can be achieved by a multiply handi-capped child also, but we may need to give different rewards and incentives from that of the sighted hearing child. When watching even a very tiny baby, one of the most striking things about his behaviour is his determination to achieve a desired object or movement. The multiply handicapped child is limited in this by his handicapping condition; his sensory input and perception of himself are necessarily governed by his dis-abilities and the help that he can be given to ameliorate these.

All children *learn by doing*. Throughout his entire child-hood, the non-handicapped child is usually given unlimited opportunities for activity, whereas the handicapped child may be limited not only by his disabilities, but by the labelling process he has undergone, which has influenced the ways in which people behave towards him. A mother recently de-scribed to me how her child is being 'taught to sign' by being taken, once a week, to the language room. Here he is shown a picture of an apple and taught to sign 'apple'. No more instruction in signing is given to him, so that effectively he is receiving communication/language/signing input for a mere fifteen minutes a week.

Daily Plan
All children need practice and the opportunity to learn more through their own activities within as normal a setting as possible. In order to provide this, it may be necessary to plan to structure the handicapped child's day, so as to give order, realistic content and meaning to his life. By formulating a

structure to his daily activities, the needs of his brothers and sisters and of the rest of the family can be incorporated.

The daily plan should not mean that the child is expected to conform rigidly to a set of rules or exercises, but simply that, within his normal daily activities, all his needs will have been planned for, taking into account his developmental needs in the following areas: motor, auditory, visual, tactile, cognitive, communication, and daily living skills such as feeding, washing, toileting, and dressing. In order to plan a reasonable programme, it is sensible first to assess what his skills are in those areas by using objective assessments as described in Chapter 2. We need to see what his present skills are so that we can build on these and, if there are gaps in his development that need to be filled, take steps to provide activities that will do this. As an example, we shall look at Aaron, who is aged three years, has extremely floppy muscles and is therefore unable to move independently, is totally blind and partially hearing. He lives at home with his mother, father and two sisters, all of whom interact with him at some point during his day.

AARON

Aaron attends the special care section of his local school, which is for children with a variety of disabilities. There are no other blind children in the school and this has to be taken into account when formulating his daily plan. Everything he needs to learn must be presented to him *differently* from the sighted children in the class; everything he meets, he will perceive in a different way from his sighted peers; and between home and school complete communication will be necessary in order to help Aaron achieve maximum independence in all of the following areas:

Motor Development

Postural Control

With any multiply handicapped child, the incentive to sit unsupported, pull from sitting to standing, and stand alone in order to move forward, is reduced because the visual input is missing. If the child also has a hearing impairment, as in

Aaron's case, this will even further reduce his incentive to sit and stand unsupported, because the sounds he hears will have little or no meaning for him and may even appear quite threatening. Our reactions to threats vary according to our disposition. Some children will become aggressive, some will retreat, some will become confused—very few will behave normally.

We also have to consider Aaron's poor muscle tone. He can sit alone when placed, but cannot maintain this posture for very long. He needs assistance and encouragement to sit for longer periods unsupported, and in order to do this it will be necessary to find cause-and-effect toys that have meaning for him, so that he will voluntarily maintain a sitting position for longer periods of time. At the moment Aaron does not have the experience of standing, and we may have to consider placing him in a standing frame, again with toys as the motivating factor to help him achieve independent standing. Toys that move *away* from Aaron are ineffective, toys that he cannot activate himself are of little value, and toys without an immediate reward, such as vibration or music, should be avoided. An extremely useful addition to any school's equipment is the Pethna range of equipment (see p. 232 for useful toys, equipment, and addresses).

Aaron needs as many opportunities as any non-handicapped child to sit and stand throughout the day, always bearing in mind that no movement is undertaken by a non-handicapped child without meaning, purpose and, usually, fun. Babies do not sit to please their mothers, they sit because they have the muscle power to enable them to do so and the visual incentive and/or auditory input that has been denied to Aaron. There are ways of overcoming his difficulties, but they take more ingenuity and planning, and need more opportunity for practice. *Anything* that works for Aaron at home should work for him at school, and vice versa. His teachers, therapists and parents must be in agreement about how to achieve his postural control, because continuity of approach for the multiply handicapped child is not just important, it is absolutely essential. He should feel that he is in control of any situation and therefore, when planning his programme, his needs as a blind child will always be at the forefront of everybody's attitudes towards the activities that are prepared for him. He will need to feel comfortable when he is sitting and standing; he will need to know where he is in space, particularly at school; he will need to have his own classroom area with which he can become completely familiar.

Locomotion

Aaron can roll and twist and sometimes propels himself along the floor, but he does not crawl forward. Many blind children never crawl, but they can be encouraged to 'scoot forward' on their bottom so as to achieve independent locomotion. The reasons why they do not crawl are manifold, but include the fact that they obviously feel much safer with as much of their bodies on the floor as possible: bottom, legs, feet and hands all in contact with the floor, probably give a much greater feeling of security than is experienced in the crawling position. Equally, when the blind child crawls he is much more likely to bump his head, thus losing any confidence he may have acquired.

Having said all this, it is important to bear in mind that Aaron needs to have the experience of being on his tummy so that he uses different muscles. An enjoyable way of giving him this experience is to place him over an adult's outstretched legs and play rhythmic singing games with him, to emphasise the fact that he is going backwards and forwards. No activity with Aaron should ever be undertaken without verbal explanations, and the more they can be accompanied by song the better for both participants, because within the rhythm of the song can be included certain essential concepts; for example, songs such as:

> Incy Wincy Spider,
> Climbing *up* the spout;
> *Down* came the rain
> And washed the spider *out*.
> *Out* came the sun
> And dried up all the rain;

Incy Wincy Spider
Climbed the spout again.

and
The grand old Duke of York,
He had ten thousand men,
He marched them *up* to the *top* of the hill
And he marched them *down* again.
And when they were *up* they were *up*,
And when they were *down* they were *down*,
And when they were only half-way up
They were neither *up* nor *down*.

and
Aaron, Aaron here you are
Sitting on my *knee*;
Aaron, Aaron here you are
Sitting on my *knee*.
(sung to the tune of 'See-saw Majorie Daw')

and
Half a pound of tuppenny rice,
Half a pound of treacle,
That's the way the money goes,
Pop goes the weasel.

and
Here we show Aaron what to do,
What to do, what to do.
Here we show Aaron what to do,
Now we're at *school/home* today.

This is the way we brush Aaron's *teeth*,
Brush Aaron's *teeth*, brush Aaron's *teeth*.
This is the way we brush Aaron's *teeth*,
Now we're at *school/home* today.
(sung to the tune of 'Here we go round the Mulberry Bush')

and
Aaron is rocking *back* and *forth*,
Aaron is rocking *back* and *forth*,
Aaron is rocking *back* and *forth*,
Playing here today.
(sung to the tune of 'Skip to my Lou')

Many other similar songs will provide incidental opportunities for demonstrating to him the meaning of words such as *up*, *down*, *out*, *knee*, *teeth*, *back* and *forth*.

Fine Motor Skills

Aaron can hold an object in his hands and will attempt to move it, but when it falls from his grasp he does not attempt to retrieve it. Many children with Aaron's difficulties need to be in contact with an object for them to know that it exists, whereas the sighted child quickly learns that when an object is released from his grasp the object itself has constancy and can be searched for, retrieved and played with again. This is why you will see sighted children playing with a posting box, and why many blind children find the activity not only meaningless but confusing. Why should the blind child (with a hearing loss) release an object into a container such as a posting box if, by his actions, he thereby loses it? We have to provide children like Aaron with opportunities for practising the same skills as their sighted hearing peers, but with their lack of sight always in the forefront of our plans. So, rather than asking Aaron to post objects, we can ask him to put them into a container which in itself gives a reward; an up-turned tambourine makes an excellent container, and when Aaron drops even quite light objects into it, they will make a very satisfying clatter. A children's plastic bucket with a silver foil food container in the bottom makes another good receptacle.

Many young multiply handicapped children do not use their fingers separately, nor do they realise that they have two hands which can be used together. It will sometimes be necessary to show Aaron, co-actively, how to transfer objects from one hand to another, and how he can use both hands to achieve a goal. Holding a drum with one hand and beating on it with a stick with the other hand; holding a musical toy in one hand while pulling on the string to activate it with the other; pressing buzzers and bells with different fingers—these are all ways to help him come to the realisation that he is capable of fine finger and different hand movements, and that both his hands can work together to manipulate an object.

There are well-documented sequences of the development of fine motor skills and no attempt has been made here to present all the stages. Incidental learning is severely limited in deaf-blind children because of their sensory impairments, so they may therefore need help in acquiring fine motor skills. The child's physical condition may have implications here, and a careful assessment will need to be made so that realistic goals can be set for each child.

Co-ordination of hand movements can be monitored by vision or touch, so the development of visual and tactile awareness is an integral part of the acquisition of fine motor skills. For children such as Aaron, who are totally blind, all fine finger movement skills will be monitored by touch. A high level of assistance will ensure that the visually impaired child persists and completes the task and, as it becomes more familiar, the level of assistance will be reduced. Once the child has developed a range of fine motor skills, he can combine these to tackle successfully more complex activities and ma-nipulate objects skilfully. Aaron will gradually be able to transfer objects from hand to hand, hold two objects in one hand, and then use different movements with either hand so as to activate cause-and-effect toys.

Because Aaron is totally blind, he will always have to be given time to explore, and plenty of time to practise acquired skills. As he progresses, he will still need help from an adult, and these interactions will provide some of the motivation that will help to maintain his interest in the activity. Some children use sight to co-ordinate hand movements, but this visual information may be supplemented with tactile input, using mouth, hands and head. Once Aaron has developed skills of reaching and grasping objects and is co-ordinating hand move-ments, the adult's role will be to give opportunities to practise and extend these skills.

With a lot of individual help and attention, Aaron should reach a level of mastery of fine motor skills. The degree of control and accuracy he has to manipulate objects, and his fine motor ability, will necessarily facilitate the development of his perceptual skills. As he moves on to more complex use of materials, he will be able to use his fine motor/perceptual skills to enrich his play activities. The enjoyment of the activity will then be its own reward and he will continue to play in the absence of the adult; thus, the level of interaction he receives from adults at his present stage will greatly enhance his skills in achieving independence later on.

The development of fine motor skills in the deaf-blind child is encouraged by the rewards and incentives chosen to replace those usually provided by vision and hearing. The motivation for each child will be different and careful choices need to be made on an individual basis. The physical abilities of each child must be considered so that what is expected is realistic. Because incidental learning is minimal and may be fragmented or disjointed, the teacher will have to make careful plans to enable the child to progress from one step to the next. Time and the opportunity to practise each developmental stage

The adult will need to demonstrate where the child is in space, so that he can gain as complete a picture of himself and his environment as possible.

should be allowed for, so that the child participates fully in the activity and skills are consolidated.

Auditory Development

Aaron is making some early communicative interaction using his voice as a means to engage the attention of adults. An important factor in the development of his auditory skills will be to attach meaning to the sounds he hears: we know that he is aware of sounds, but do we know that he can identify them, comprehend them and remember what they are so that, when he hears them again, he will be able to relate them to his past experiences? Awareness of sound is simply knowing that it exists, but beyond this Aaron must be helped to recognise what he hears, otherwise his environment will be meaningless for most of the time.

In order to assist Aaron, it is necessary to ask those around him to become aware of environmental, everyday sounds and to give him some indication in a conversational way every time a sound occurs; this will help him to structure and comprehend what is going on around him. It is usually easier to assist any blind child who is not yet speaking to identify and recognise sounds if he is in a quiet room with no background or extraneous sound, and often the best place to provide this type of experience is the home; in a busy classroom it is sometimes impossible to reorganise all the other children's work schedules without disrupting them, and so the blind child is expected to conform in the sighted hearing child's world.

Unless Aaron can be given a quiet corner or quiet times with his teacher, it will be quite confusing for him to hear the busy noises of the normally active classroom. This is why, when a blind child goes to a school for a variety of handicapped children, it is so important to stress to all the people working with him that he has different needs from the sighted children, particularly if he is not yet speaking and cannot ask, 'What is that noise?' An adult must always be on hand to identify the noises for him, as he will never pick up clues about his environment unless this is done at this early stage. Attention involves mental concentration and, unless his attention is drawn to sounds by someone saying, 'Aaron, listen, do you hear the . . . ?' he will quickly become bored or may otherwise withdraw from the learning situation. Once his attention has been drawn to the sounds, he will begin to listen actively. It will be possible to see that he is interested, because his demeanour will show that he is making a conscious effort to hear and interpret the sounds around him.

This listening stage will lead him on towards the ability to imitate. At first, perhaps, he will imitate the banging of a drum, initially joining in co-actively and later being able to listen to certain rhythms which the teacher or adult provides for him and then beating the drum in response and in imitation. He can then be encouraged to search for sound-makers, such as a tin with dried peas in it, a carton with dry rice in it, or different sorts of bells. The latter can sometimes produce pleasing results very quickly, as they will emit a ringing sound with little effort on his part. Once he has learnt to enjoy sound-makers, he will be encouraged to discriminate between them—for example, between the ringing of a bell and the banging of a drum. This will lead on to being able to indicate, by the movement of his arm, head or hand, where he believes the sound is coming from, then to further interest in sound, and so on.

Awareness through listening should become part of Aaron's everyday programme. Any common environmental sound can be identified: when someone knocks at the front door, ask them to keep knocking and take Aaron to the door saying, 'Aaron, can you hear that knocking? Someone is knocking at our door. Let's open the door. Oh, it's Daddy, he was knocking at our door!' Remember that blind children do not know the cause of the many effects within their environment; the only way they can cope with the insecurity of things 'just happening' is to ignore them.

We must encourage everyone who meets Aaron to help him realise that all sounds are real and that they have meaning. This should be applied to all the sounds in the environment that come within his physical limitations. He should be encouraged each time to listen and then to discover the source of the sound. At first this will be done co-actively and will be quite difficult for him to remember, but as time goes by it will be a perfectly natural adjunct to his daily plan. Everyone who comes in contact with Aaron should realise that his environment is, at the moment, a meaningless blur of sound, but that he is ready and willing to learn more if he is given the opportunity to do so. All the sounds which have meaning to the sighted hearing child such as a bell, a buzzer, a telephone, a helicopter, an aeroplane, a refrigerator, a washing machine, will have to be described until you are *sure* he knows what they are.

When we think of a non-handicapped three-year-old child, we expect him to start to use the phrase 'what's that?' Very often young children go through an intense phase when they are constantly asking questions, because they are eagerly anticipating answers from adults. This intense questioning period can often last for months and the weary parent can sometimes feel that it will last for years. With the multiply handicapped or blind child this period can become extremely delayed or distorted, because the adults who *should* be naming the objects and people that are encountered in the child's environment simply omit to do so. People forget the need to introduce themselves to the young multiply handicapped child, presuming that somehow he knows who they are. This can cause unnecessary confusion for the child. We must always try to imagine how it feels to be multiply handicapped, and to give as many clues as we can to help our children process information which we may sometimes take for granted.

Very often people will approach Aaron, not realising that they must *identify* themselves so that he knows who is speaking to him. (Sometimes our children must feel like wearing a badge that says, 'You know who I am, but I don't know who you are. Tell me first before you expect me to respond.') Multiply handicapped children must find the world a very strange place, where things suddenly happen to them and people appear and disappear with very little warning. For example, Aaron might be going to go out for a walk. His coat is put on, and then suddenly the adult who is with him remembers that she has not turned off the tap, so he is put down very quickly and left for a few moments (all right for the sighted child but very confusing for Aaron). The adult may then reappear and pick Aaron up again, then realise that it is too hot for him to wear a coat and take it off again—all of which, although very straightforward to the sighted child, must seem an odd set of sequences to Aaron. Remembering to give clear explanations is not easy for the adult, but how difficult it must be for any child not to know *exactly* what is happening to him.

There will be times when it will be quite legitimate for Aaron to join in games that can be played with a few children. For instance, he would probably get a great deal of pleasure from sharing musical activities with a small group of children, but the children's names *must* be identified and likewise the musical instruments they are going to play, and at first all the children would have to take it in turns to play with the teacher introducing them, thus: 'Mark is playing the bell,' Mark rings the bell; 'Tom is playing the drum,' Tom plays the drum; 'Fred is playing the kazoo,' Fred plays the kazoo; 'James is playing the piano,' James plays the piano; and 'Aaron is playing the tambourine.' Ideally, at first, the children will always be introduced in the same way and in the same order, so that Aaron begins to retain some identifying feature about each child and his instrument; again, it is so easy for the sighted child to do this and so very difficult for children like Aaron who are deprived of their one main channel of information: sight. Aaron must learn everything in ways which are usually *completely* different from that of sighted children. This is very easy to say, but usually extremely difficult to put into practice when teachers are busy and there are other children who have a legitimate claim on their time.

Once Aaron is showing awareness of sounds of various kinds, all kinds of activities are possible. Within his daily plan, he can have a sound-making time when the adult makes different noises, perhaps with a bell, tambourine, drum, hooter or kazoo, so that he can listen for different sounds, rhythms and songs. Knowing sound from silence is also important. Good rhythmic records or tapes can be played, and Aaron can be helped to clap or move to the music. It may be necessary to

institute a few signals or gestures or signs for him, so that he
starts to associate certain words with certain actions; we felt
that the following signals would be helpful:
—finished/bye-bye (so that Aaron knows when someone is
  leaving him, or when an activity is finished);
—more (so that he knows when an activity will continue);
—drink;
—eat;
—toilet.
It should be noted that signs do not replace words, but help
people to understand more about the language that is being
presented to them. It is important to remember never to
substitute a sign for a word, but that sometimes a sign, if used
correctly, will give meaning to a word which otherwise the
child would have difficulty in understanding.

Tactile Development
Aaron responds to being warm. He permits soft, smooth
textures to be rubbed on his hands, feet or body, and moves his
hands, feet or body over smooth, soft textures. He reacts to
tactile stimulation by body movement; he permits his hands,
feet or body to be moved over unfamiliar, rough-textured
surfaces, and moves his hands, feet or body over unfamiliar
rough-textured surfaces. He explores objects with his fingers.

He needs to become bodily aware and, by providing him
with more experiences with water, sand or soft-textured materials, or through the use of massage, movement to music or
movement over different surfaces, he will not only be encouraged to become tactually aware but his communication level
and development will be greatly enhanced; the more aware
you are of yourself in space and of your relationship to it, the
more you are aware of your limbs as part of yourself, and the
more able you will be to use your body with understanding in
different situations.

Cognition, Communication and Language
It must be remembered that communication is taking place at
some level throughout Aaron's day and is not a skill taught in

Opportunities for close one-to-one interaction and communication are provided within the child's normal range of abilities and interests . . . learning to 'sign' *jump*.

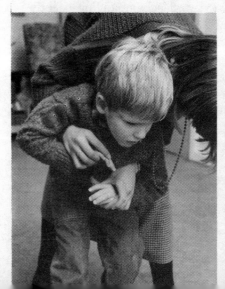

isolation. Building trusting relationships and interacting with the environment are the basic skills from which communication will develop. These skills can then be extended and modified to the point at which Aaron can influence and control his world by a formal means of communication, that is a language, whether spoken or signed. We need to be very sensitive to Aaron's attempts to communicate, as the signals he gives may be no more than very small changes in behaviour. Signals can range from a 'stilling' in Aaron, or just a slight movement of any part of his body, to gross movements indicating pleasure or displeasure. Sometimes you need to know the child very well to be able to interpret the signal correctly. Aaron's wriggle shows his enjoyment of activities.

Imitation has a part to play in the development of communication. This begins with the adult imitating the child, either vocally or physically, to show him that this is an acceptable pattern of behaviour and to reinforce a sound or signal as a valid form of communication.

Manual signs are an alternative form of language particularly appropriate for children whose sensory impairments are such that speech is either severely delayed or unlikely to develop. Signs should be used in context throughout the day, repeated often and always accompanied by speech. Signs can be used from an early age, so that Aaron can become familiar with the language before he is ready to use it as a means of expression. Appropriate context and accompanying speech must always apply when teaching signs. Initially this is a tactile experience, with the adult positioned behind Aaron. In this way as much physical contact as possible is given to convey the maximum amount of tactile information. The guiding of Aaron's movements should be firm and unhurried. Communication can be encouraged by building up a secure relationship, and the adult will need to observe Aaron closely for body signals that indicate any interaction. Other communication skills, including physical and vocal imitation, can be encouraged to play situations. We need to give Aaron an appropriate form of language which may mean the use of manual signs used from an early age.

Preparing the Daily Plan

The non-handicapped child receives almost as much information from external factors as he does from the adults with whom he is in closest contact: the television, brothers and sisters, his peer group, books and comics, radio and newspapers; through these external factors he learns, almost incidentally, about the world beyond his immediate environment. Although, of course, his parents and teachers make careful plans for his work and play, they do not have to structure their thinking to the extent often required for the parents and teachers of multiply handicapped children. Children with severe sensory impairment are usually unable to learn incidentally from their environment and, indeed, they need to be introduced to their environment in a completely different way from their sighted hearing peers. We must always bear in mind the normal developmental sequences when planning for the needs of the multiply handicapped child. The non-handicapped child would experience:

1 *Communication*. He would recognise that, as well as language, the facial expression, the set of the body, the change in attitude, gestures and tone of voice would all assist him in understanding what was being talked about.

2 *Self-Help Skills—dressing, eating, washing, toileting*. The non-handicapped child would have incentives for learning these skills, which would include the pleasure in the activity itself and very often the ability to imitate his peers. A highly motivating factor in achieving self-help skills would be adult's approval of a skill mastered.

3 *Play*. Play is a child's means of learning, and all non-handicapped children start learning from the moment they are born. Very often the adults whom he meets structure the child's environment towards his needs and abilities through the play activities which they provide.

4 *Interaction*. The non-handicapped child learns very quickly the pleasure he can receive from other people; he responds when he is talked to and when he is smiled at, when he touches and is touched. He learns to co-ordinate

his hands and body and therefore interacts very quickly with his environment, learning often quite incidentally about texture, how things work and the properties of objects.

5 *Visual Skills, Motor Skills, Auditory Skills.* All of these skills in the non-handicapped child follow the same developmental pattern and gradually refine, so that by the time the child goes to school he is able to walk and run and make himself understood, using quite sophisticated language, and can sometimes read his own name.

6 *Cognitive Development.* The non-handicapped child will have received incidental information which has helped him to develop his ability to think and plan. He will have had enough experiences of normal life to appreciate that there is a structure to his world and those of other people. He will have seen that each day has a certain sequence of events: waking up, getting up, washing, teeth cleaning, dressing, etc., and he will have appreciated that there are constancies and recurring events that give order, structure, content and meaning to his life.

The multiply handicapped or deaf-blind child does not have the same clues and opportunities for incidental learning as the non-handicapped child, so the teacher and parent must plan carefully to make his day equally alive and meaningful. As an example, we can look at Sally Silverman's time-table for a four-year-old girl:

Rana's Day

Off the Bus. Rana's name is called before she is touched and then handled slowly, so as to give her time to appreciate her teacher's greeting.

Carried. Close contact is essential; this gives a sense of well-being at the start of the day.

Stopping. At the doorway, Rana is given time to feel the change in the air-flow.

Trailing. Rana needs me to put her hand to the wall as we move along, to stop at landmarks (the fish tank, the mirror).

Listening. This allows time for Rana to pick out the sounds of her own classroom.

Consistent Positioning. Doors and furniture should remain in the same place; the door should be closed so that we can push it open together.

Self-Help. The need for gross physical prompts—take her hand to her zip, feel the coldness, listen to the 'zzzzzzz', find her coat peg together.

Toileting. An excellent learning environment for Rana: olfactory clues—her sudocream, her friend's talc; auditory clues —my shoes sound different on the tiles, her personal music-box is playing by her potty; visual clues—the height from the changing table to the ceiling is only a few feet, and while I am seeing to her nappy, she is catching a glimmer of the glittery paper above her. A perfect place for putting my face close to hers, brief eye contact. Listen to the sound of the toilet flushing.

Greeting Session. Rana sits very close to the other children and is encouraged to reach out for their hands, my face, the strings of the guitar as I sing her 'hello' song.

Milk Time. Collecting the bottles from the crate with me; being helped to be aware of the slightly wet/cold glass, the weight of it; being helped to clink two together to let the rest of the group know that the bottles are on their way. Visual awareness—look at the shiny milk bottle top, tilt it in the sunlight.

Changing Position. Enclosed spaces where her own sounds will bounce back to her and where objects will not roll out of her very limited reach. She needs constant verbal reassurance and sound clues as to where I am in the room; also needs me to listen and pay attention to all her sounds.

Movement Time. All children with a visual handicap need extra attention to 'feeding in' body awareness. We slide and roll Rana on furry mats, a velvety mat, and on our legs and stomachs. She needs to experience fast, free-flow movements in our arms, as she will never observe them or be able to initiate them of her own volition.

Visual Stimulation. Coloured spots and other lighting effects are used to highlight body parts, to make shadows and to create a mood.

Quiet Time. On the air mattress with our nursery nurse on one side and her friend Samira on the other. Rana is in control of her environment. She is relaxed and reaches out to feel Helen's face, and smiles.

Dinner Time. A quiet environment is essential. She needs to pick up sound and olfactory clues (footsteps coming, the dinner being cut up). She needs to be told what she is eating and to smell before the spoon is put to her mouth; to touch her food, be helped to feel her empty dish.

Washing. An activity designed to incorporate almost all the curriculum areas appropriate for Rana at her stage of development. She stands up to a sink with the use of a flexi-stand (being presented with a wet flannel makes meaningful connections hard when you can't see where the wetness has come from); her attention is directed to the shininess of the tap (an angle-poise lamp is used to highlight her washing materials and the sink and water).

Self Image. Rana's sighted friends are starting to realise that they have a reflected image in the bathroom mirror. Rana needs us to put her hand to her mouth to feel the teeth she is about to brush, to put her hand to her hair to feel its length and how glossy it is.

Afternoon Activities. Moving her fingers in a pool of pink hand cream makes a change from finger paints; with the overhead lighting off and with the angle-poise directed on Rana's hands, she has more chance of making visual contact with the smelly substance between her fingers.

Preparation for Home. Rana needs physical prompting to wave 'bye-bye'; I also put her hand over my wrist when I do it and put her hand to my mouth when I say it. We trail the same route back to her bus-stop, then stop and listen for the engine sounds of her own bus. When she is safely in her seat and is reassured by the familiar noises of the other children, driver and coach guide, I tell her that I am going to go now and will be seeing her in the morning.

Having given order and structure to the child's day, we can now consider how to structure the child's week so that this, too, will be seen as a recurring series of events. One way to achieve this is to provide a tactual time-table or, if the child can see well enough, pictorial diagrams can be substituted in place of the tactual time-table.

Tactual Time-table
A small article of clothing, or a piece of apparatus which can be used to represent an activity for a particular day of the week, may be used for this time-table.

Example
Monday is a day on which the child goes to school, so a school bag identical to the one the child uses can provide an excellent tactual clue for the first day of the school week.
Tuesday. On Tuesday the child goes swimming, so a towel, or a piece of towel, or a swimming costume, can be used as a tactual clue.
Wednesday . . . and so on.

When structuring the child's day for learning and play, it is essential to bear in mind that all the activities provided should encourage the child to achieve maximum independence in all fields. Every child needs an individual structure that will enable him to achieve his highest possible level of learning and should give plenty of time to build on and practise the skills he already has. This will almost always mean co-ordinating all the work done with him at school, so that his parents can reinforce any new skill that he has been taught by his teachers. Constant communication is essential between all the adults responsible for the multiply handicapped child's care and education, because, unlike the non-handicapped child, the child with a dual sensory impairment is unable, until he is much older, to report back on any new learning he has achieved; the deaf-blind child will rely on the interactions of his caring adults to ensure complete continuity of approach.

9 Behaviour Problems and Some Solutions

It is sad and disturbing to see any child deliberately trying to hurt himself, but unfortunately self-abusive and destructive behaviour can often become a part of the multiply handicapped child's life. It is important to question why this behaviour should occur, for if we know why it occurs we know how to prevent it from happening.

Yet again we need to look at the non-handicapped sighted hearing child for our reference. It is perfectly normal for a young baby to rock and bounce, to wave his hands in the air in front of him, to giggle and croon to himself and to find pleasure and amusement from his own body. It is a charming sight to see the young baby playing with his toes, trying to bite them, and to watch how determinedly he discovers his feet through playing with them. Many young babies rock themselves to sleep, banging their heads on the pillow for comfort; many children (and remember we are talking about non-handicapped or 'normal' children) suck their fingers, bite their quicks, twiddle their hair, take a comfort blanket to bed, suck dummies, have tantrums, reject new experiences and play to the gallery.

We do not consider any of these behaviours inappropriate in normal children, if they are related to age and stage. At the age of two or three, it is perfectly normal to have a tantrum in the supermarket because you think your mother should provide you with sweets; it is not so normal when the child is still doing this at the age of seven or eight. Behaviour is only a problem when you see the action as being inappropriate, harmful to the child or others, not age- and stage-related, or when it stops the child from taking part in other, more appropriate activities.

Behaviour problems must have a reason; they do not start or stop for nothing.

Let us take as an example a blind and hard of hearing child whose parents are constantly pressing him to achieve more than he is capable of doing. He will have a choice of several reactions. No one, least of all his parents, should be surprised when he reacts by screaming; his parents have driven him to despair. Our reaction when we meet a child who screams should be to ask ourselves what it is that he is screaming about, why he has been driven to that state, and how we can help him to react in a more acceptable way.

If a child is attention-seeking, then he should be given attention, because somewhere in his life he is missing the attention that all people need. In a busy classroom or home it is often difficult to organise a programme for a child who is seeking attention by screaming. One way to provide for his emotional needs (unless he can be given a one-to-one adult-to-child ratio) is to ensure that he will be given close physical contact at *set* points during the day, and that, however much he does or does not scream, those times are his by right; they need not be earned because love does not need to be earned. The attention-seeking child always has a reason for his behaviour.

If the child throws objects to seek attention, this can be much more dangerous and difficult to manage than the screaming child, because the object itself may be of value or, worse, may hurt another person. It is, again, important to look at the child before you can effectively eliminate the behaviour. Has he (or the object) received so much attention through throwing that his behaviour has been inadvertently re-inforced? Has he been told firmly that he should not throw objects? This question is not lightly asked, because many people have been advised to ignore tantrums or attention-seeking behaviour; they have therefore not conveyed to the child the inadvisability of throwing, nor has the child been shown the consequence of his actions. The maxim should be: 'if you throw it you pick it up'. And a further maxim should be: 'if it breaks, it takes even longer to pick it up'. In other words, giving the child the right information about the consequence of his actions, and being absolutely firm every time it happens, will usually eliminate this behaviour.

If the throwing is random and not for attention-seeking reasons, it may be due to the fact that the child does not see the purpose of the object that he has thrown. Blind children do not have the same concepts of toys or objects if they are unable to hear about them as well as see them. What to you appears to be a pretty flower is a soft, rather unpleasant, perhaps prickly object for the blind-deaf child, which he needs to get rid of as quickly as possible.

Biting and sucking of hands can often start because the child is trying to comfort himself, and what starts as simple comfort behaviour can become an ingrained habit if the warmth and security he is seeking is not provided. Many people would say that you must be quite desperate for attention if you are sucking and biting your hands so obsessively that you have no time for other activities. Before making such judgements we should look to see how many activities are available for the child to take part in. If there are no other legitimate activities that he can successfully achieve *by himself*, then his only toy will be his own body and the uses to which he can put it. Masturbation is no more common in multiply handicapped children than in others, but it is much more understandable if the child has no other outlets for his energies. Biting and sucking hands can also be thought of as defensive mechanisms, for if the child has his hands in his mouth he may feel that he will not be asked to take part in activities that frighten and confuse him. If he is left alone these habits are bound to recur; elimination can only be started when we increase the adult/child contact, until he has learnt that he is part of a world that offers him exciting alternatives to occupy his hands.

We therefore need to show the child who is biting or sucking his hands a variety of other experiences which he can take part in and which he will enjoy as much as his old preferred self-stimulatory behaviour. With the young child, we would start by showing him how much he is loved and how much he can trust the adult, by close one-to-one contact, entering into his world in as gentle and reassuring a way as possible, rocking him like a baby and gradually holding his hands away from his mouth. If the adult can devote considerable time to the child, if the child has learnt to trust his care-giver, and if the situation which made him seek such attention and bodily comfort does not recur, then the next stages of mutual trust and confidence will follow.

Head-banging, eye-poking, eye-pressing, scratching, pinching and rocking can usually be found to have similar causes: the child has had to turn inwards on himself for stimulation because the outside world has not presented as satisfying or stimulating an occupation as his own body.

To prevent parents and teachers from feeling guilty about these mannerisms, it should be said that they are more likely to occur in the child with impaired vision and hearing because his opportunities for other, legitimate activities are so much more limited. It should also be said that, often, none of these

Eye-pressing.

behaviours need occur in the young child, as with so much more knowledge about the value of early stimulation programmes, parents, teachers and therapists can aim to prevent them becoming a habit. In this case it is always true to say that prevention is better than cure (and a lot easier).

Eye-pressing often starts when the child is aged one year to 18 months. At first, many parents mistakenly believe that the child's eyes are sore or that he is tired, and do not realise that he is merely deriving pleasure and comfort from pressing his eyes. To be sure that his eyes are not hurting him and that an important aspect of his eye condition has not been missed, they should take him to the ophthalmologist as soon as the eye-pressing starts; if the ophthalmologist can confirm that nothing further requires attention, then they should be aware that this habit may be starting and take every possible step to eliminate it. Some experts feel that further damage can be caused to the eye if it is constantly pressed, and this in itself should be a good enough reason to take preventive action.

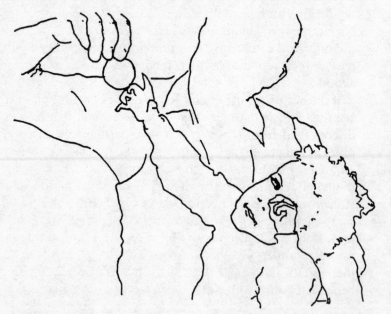

Substituting pleasurable activities to discourage eye-pressing.

Certainly, a child who constantly eye-presses may develop large, discoloured rings around his eyes, making him look more handicapped than he actually is.

It is important never to over-react when trying to eliminate or prevent any mannerism or habit in the young child, since you might then replace it with a much more dangerous or offensive behaviour problem. Thus, when trying to stop eye-pressing, the best way is gently and without comment to remove the child's hand from his eye, giving him a toy with which he enjoys playing to substitute for the eye-pressing activity. If attention is drawn to the eye-pressing and the child feels that this is an important activity that can gain attention, he may well increase rather than decrease the behaviour. For example, Zachary, who is totally blind, received praise from his mother every time he took his hand away from his eye, being told what a good boy he was. Because Zachary enjoyed such praise, he started to press his eye even more, drawing attention to it by calling to his mother, saying, 'Good boy, Zachary, take your hand away from your eye,' so that she would give him more praise and attention. It was only when his mother thought about her behaviour that she realised that the best way of dealing with this problem was to substitute pleasurable activities, rather than unwittingly praising the action.

If the eye-pressing persists because it has become an unconscious habit, it may take longer to stop than if it had been discouraged from the start. Some experts would say that it takes as long to change a habit as it takes to develop it. To use an analogy from the diet-conscious world, it will take determined effort, much exercise and constant dieting to lose five stones of excess weight, and it takes very little effort and not a scrap of willpower to lose five ounces! In other words, try to look at the child's behaviour objectively; if you find that any of his behaviour is bizarre or would appear so to the outsider, then usually it is worth deciding to change it now, before it has become too difficult and time-consuming to alter.

Benjamin

If people have become so used to the child's behaviour that they do not see it as a problem, then there is no possibility of altering it; the co-operation of most adults in the child's life, not just some of them, will be needed before remedial measures can be completely successful. As an example, Zachary used to blow 'raspberries' and was content to do this for much of the day, until his mother decided that, unless he changed his habit, he would never want to do anything more constructive. So she worked very effectively at eliminating the behaviour by explaining to Zachary that he could only blow 'raspberries' on his bed, where they would be tolerated, but that they would never be accepted in any other situation. Unfortunately, Zachary's uncle thought that blowing 'raspberries' was very amusing, and so encouraged him in the behaviour by getting him to copy more and more peculiar sounds. If we have conflict of interest in the family situation, where one parent is trying to achieve a certain standard of behaviour and another parent or relative is in opposition to this or gives tacit approval to the undesirable behaviour, then the family must resolve this before anything can be achieved.

Benjamin's eye-pressing was described as constant, occurring even when he was participating in activities that both he and his parents and relatives enjoyed. Benjamin's father did not feel it was a problem as he was so used to his son's behaviour that he had stopped noticing it—although he would certainly have commented had he seen either of his other two sons pressing their eyes. He had to be shown that Benjamin's eye-pressing was preventing him from fully participating in some activities, because he would only occasionally use both hands together, one hand usually being occupied in the eye-pressing activity. The solution to the problem was simple, but it required both parents to discuss and agree on it first.

It is important to discuss the behaviour in some detail and to explore feelings about the problem. Once everyone has decided to take action, the next stage is to achieve this as quickly and as effectively as possible. The first step can be to set out exactly what the behaviour is in objective terms, and then to record this behaviour and when it occurs. Often, when discussing bizarre or problematic behaviour, with parents, they feel that it occurs throughout the day; when this behaviour is analysed, however, they discover that there is a pattern to it, and that it occurs as the direct result of a situation which the child tries to control by resorting to self-stimulatory activities. If a child feels unsure or threatened because he is uncertain about what is happening to him within his environment, he may feel he has to suck or bite his hands, bang his head with his hands or bang his head on any hard surface, totally refuse to co-operate by screaming or crying or curling up into a ball and withdrawing from the activity, or trying to isolate himself by other means. This type of behaviour should not be seen to be

BEHAVIOUR CHART

Child's Name:	Benjamin
Recording Adult's names:	Benjamin's mother (9–5) and father (5–7)
Behaviour to be recorded:	Benjamin's eye pressing
Direction:	tick if Benjamin presses his eye
	o if Benjamin does not press his eye
Record:	throughout the day for one week

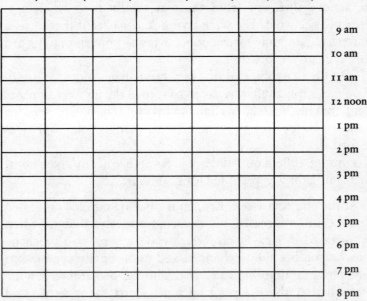

Sunday	Monday	Tuesday	Wednesday	Thursday	Friday	Saturday	
							9 am
							10 am
							11 am
							12 noon
							1 pm
							2 pm
							3 pm
							4 pm
							5 pm
							6 pm
							7 pm
							8 pm

insoluble, but the child needs to feel completely secure before it is eliminated altogether. Behaviour such as Benjamin's made it difficult for him to participate fully in the activities which were given him; for whatever reason they arose, they needed to be eliminated in order to help him make any further progress. The idea of writing down *exactly* what the behaviour was proved very helpful to Benjamin's parents. They were then able to formulate objectively what it was they wished to achieve with their child. In order to do this, they were given a behaviour chart which they were asked to record for a period of a week.

The behaviour chart was filled in as follows:

Benjamin's Name.
Date
Adult's Name. The adult who was going to record the chart was asked to fill in his or her name.
Behaviour. Benjamin's behaviour was recorded in objective terms thus: Benjamin presses his left hand to his left eye.
Direction. The aim on this behaviour chart was to record Benjamin's behaviour. The adult's behaviour to Benjamin should remain the same, so she had to try not to use any words or actions different from those normally used when eye-pressing occurred. We were trying to discover if there was a pattern to Benjamin's behaviour, so it was important to record this as clearly as possible.
How Often. At the end of every hour, from 9.00 a.m. until 7.00 p.m., the adult was asked to record the number of times Benjamin had pressed his hand to his eye. If he had pressed his hand to his eye for the whole hour, then 'whole hour' was recorded.
Recording. If Benjamin did not press his eye in any given hour, then a nought was recorded for that hour.

At the end of a week, Benjamin's behaviour chart revealed that he never pressed his eye continuously, that he often eye-pressed during mealtimes, always eye-pressed when he was having his nappy changed and occasionally eye-pressed when his grandmother came to the house. Benjamin's parents realised that the eye-pressing had occurred for very good reasons; they felt that he pressed his eye during mealtimes so as to avoid eating the savoury course, when he was having his nappy changed because he felt unsure of the situation, and when his grandmother came to the house because he did not meet her regularly and so was perhaps rather fearful in this relatively strange situation.

The next step was to help Benjamin's parents to eliminate the eye-pressing. It was explained to them that if this behaviour (which was clearly pleasurable to Benjamin) was to be eliminated, another, equally pleasurable activity would have to be substituted. Blind children have less choice of activity than sighted children, and so they are almost bound to use their bodies for pleasure and stimulation. Rocking of the head and body, movements of the hands or head, vigorous breathing, tooth-grinding, scratching and rubbing the skin, light-gazing, eye-poking, masturbation, hair-twirling, screaming, outbursts of laughter and face slapping are all behaviours that can be observed in handicapped children and adults. The reasons why these behaviours arise must be seen to be as important as the activities themselves, because if the cause is not eliminated the activity will continue. Some causes of maladaptive behaviour are to seek comfort, to reduce anxiety, to increase stimulation, to avoid stress, or to gain added attention. As stated previously, if a child is seeking attention then I feel that child must be given attention (although not in response to the maladaptive behaviour). If a child has withdrawn into an autistic-like state, then he probably needs even more attention. If he spends prolonged periods alone, he is bound to seek stimulation in one way or another, and if he is not stimulated actively he is bound either to withdraw completely or to show his feelings of rejection and anger by what are sometimes called aggressive acts.

It is interesting to speculate what we as adults would do if we were left to despair. The behaviour which we would manifest would properly be called righteous anger, and we must bear this in mind when thinking about bizarre behaviour. Children whose main channels of information are damaged often have no other means of relating to the world, so their behaviour should be seen as a manifestation of the world's actions towards them and their reactions to this world. Benjamin's parents would have been shocked to learn that his eye-pressing behaviour need not have occurred, and that few blindisms and mannerisms need be manifested in the young child.

Having filled in their behaviour chart and analysed it objectively, Benjamin's parents were asked how they felt they could work towards eliminating his eye-pressing behaviour. If parents are not consulted at every stage, then no programme will be truly successful, and many parents are able to contribute valuable ideas towards their child's progress. It was agreed that the three occasions when Benjamin most frequently pressed his eye occurred for different reasons, and that he would need different approaches for each occasion. His parents felt that if they gave Benjamin his pudding first, so that he knew he was going to enjoy his meal, that might eliminate this behaviour at mealtimes. After discussion it was decided that, as Benjamin always ate a good breakfast and supper, it was acceptable to reverse the pudding and savoury courses at lunchtime, and indeed this solved the problem. The eye-pressing when Benjamin was having his nappy changed was eliminated by:

1 giving Benjamin far more warning about nappy-changing times through speech and gesture;
2 avoiding changing his nappy on surfaces of which he was unsure (previously he had had his nappy changed anywhere in the house);
3 changing his nappy at regular intervals—for example, always before and after a meal so that he would begin to associate mealtimes with nappy changing.

It was more difficult to decide how to eliminate Benjamin's eye-pressing when his grandmother came to the house, because she would have been very hurt had she realised that Benjamin was fearful when she came to see him. We therefore felt that Benjamin should associate his grandmother with certain toys and activities which only they shared, and that these activities should be extremely pleasurable for both of them. It was also felt that if his grandmother could come to see him more often he would become more used to her, and would thus be able to look forward to a pleasurable change in his routine. The family decided that, as Benjamin's grandmother always wore a certain perfume, they would buy a bottle of it and that, a few minutes before she came to the house, they would let him smell it, so that he might begin to associate this extremely pleasant aroma with his visitor. They also decided that, as his grandmother was rather sedentary, she would always share a music and singing session with him. Thus Benjamin's behaviour chart for the second week was filled in as follows:

Benjamin's name.
Date.
Recording Adult's name.
Behaviour. Benjamin presses his left hand to his left eye.
Direction. The aim on this behaviour chart is to record the adults' behaviour. We have discovered that Benjamin presses his eye during mealtimes, when his nappy is being changed and when his grandmother comes to the house. This week we are trying to alter some of the reasons why Benjamin presses his eye. We are trying to discover if we can help to eliminate this behaviour by slightly altering his environment.
How Often. At lunchtimes, Benjamin's pudding will be given to him first. His breakfast and supper will remain the same as before. At the end of lunchtime, record whether or not Benjamin has pressed his hand to his eye.

Benjamin will only have his nappy changed on a surface that is familiar to him, i.e. except in emergencies, always on the bathroom changing table. The same tactual clues will always be used to warn Benjamin that his nappy is about to be changed. (We agreed that his parents would tickle Benjamin's tummy, then put their hands on both sides of his nappy, to warn him that nappy-changing time was about to start. As Benjamin has a hearing loss we felt that it was important to speak and sign to him, using the same phrases and signs for all dressing and undressing activities.)

Benjamin's grandmother will be asked to come to the house three times a week instead of twice, as at present. (As she always comes for tea, we felt that this would be another clue for Benjamin to associate with his grandmother's visit.) Benjamin's grandmother will always be asked to spend half an hour at the beginning of her visit chatting to her daughter-in-law before going to speak to Benjamin, so that he gets used to the idea of having her in the house. Benjamin will then spend the next half-hour of her visit in a music and singing session with her.

Recording. As three behaviours were being recorded, Benjamin's parents filled in three separate charts: one for mealtimes, one for nappy changing times and one for grandmother's visits.

It will be seen that helping parents to analyse their child's behaviour objectively, to participate fully in planning how to alter the behaviour and in looking at their own behaviour in relation to the child, is far more useful to them and their child

James had a total obsession with light-gazing.

than just offering suggestions without being fully cognisant of the situation. Habitual mannerisms can become obsessive and, in time, become a real problem as the child grows older.

Eye-poking and light-gazing are often associated with deaf-blind children (particularly with rubella damaged children) but, as has been stated in Chapter 3, these behaviours need not be seen in children who have been given early medical attention, who have been fitted with contact lenses and hearing aids while they were young, and who have taken part in appropriate early learning intervention programmes. Unfortunately older children may be so obsessed with their own self-stimulation that it is very difficult indeed to reach them and to help them relate to the outside world. Three such children are James, Thomas and Daisy. (These children were worked with in previous Centres.)

James

James was aged eight when I met him, and his interest in light was completely absorbing. A child with light perception and a moderate to severe hearing loss, he had become so totally obsessed by light that he would search for it everywhere and would bang his head if not allowed to be close to the brightest light source in the room. Although he was interested in food, he would ignore it completely if he was seated under a light or by a window in a sunny room.

When looking at children's maladaptive behaviour the useful rule is to observe the child, his environment and his reactions to the adults or children within that environment, to ascertain whether adaptations or modifications should be made to the environment by the adult. Note that, initially, I do not ask the child to modify his behaviour. Rather, we should ask ourselves what has gone wrong in the child's past or is wrong in his present situation to cause him to manifest this behaviour. We need to adapt ourselves to him, as well as asking him to adapt to us. (Behaviour adaptation programmes usually require a little modification from everyone as well.)

We decided that, for the time being, James should not sit in rooms with overhead lighting, that we should aim to change his obsession with light-gazing in a negative fashion and transfer this interest in light towards more positive activity. We altered the fitments in the classroom and dining-room so that there was only diffuse light. Next, we bought several torches with different types of switch and coloured bulbs and, co-actively, showed James how they worked. James began to understand and appreciate that he could have fun activating the torches, and squealed with delight the first time he managed to switch one on all by himself. We had now established three important points in James's programme:

1   He had managed to activate a switch to gain a reward.
2   A reward system (activating torchlight) was now possible.
3   He could be taught to operate other switches to obtain other effects.

We then chose activities in which we felt James would enjoy participating, and decided to use light to highlight certain other activities, to act as a stimulus to his participation. He was encouraged to take part in classroom and mealtime activities by always having the activity or the meal well lit, and he was usually rewarded for positive behaviour by being allowed to play with toys with either a light or sound reward. (Some recommended toys which have a cause-and-effect principle, using switches, light and sound, are described in Chapter 10.)

Thomas
Thomas's problem proved far more difficult to eliminate. Like James, he was obsessed by light but also used to poke his eyes and bang his face, rock backwards and forwards and bang his head on any convenient hard surface. At the time of referral, he was aged nine years and had had to be excluded from his special school because his behaviour was becoming dangerous to other children as well as to his teachers. He lived alone with his widowed mother who could no longer cope with his destructive habits. I asked her to describe how she managed his behaviour and she described her efforts with Thomas as follows:

1   In order to stop him from hurting himself when he banged his head, she had provided him with a mattress-covered area in his bedroom. Two mattresses were on the wall and one was on the floor, giving him a triangular-shaped area in which to bang his head.

2   In order to prevent him from poking his eyes and banging his head, she would restrain him by holding him tightly against her body and holding his hands very tightly against his sides.

3   In order to prevent him from damaging his eyes when he poked them, she would distract him by giving him snacks and sweets at any time through the day, because she felt that if he was occupied in eating he would not poke his eyes and damage them further.

I carefully recorded his mother's response to the behaviour and, having discussed this with her and given her time to think about our observations, she agreed that, in fact, she was constantly reinforcing Thomas's behaviour. She was giving him extra opportunities to bang his head by providing the mattress-covered area in his bedroom; she was giving him extra attention by restraining him and holding his hands; and she was rewarding him by providing him with sweets and snacks as a distraction. I felt that, had Thomas's teachers been aware of his mother's reactions to his destructive behaviour, they would have been able to suggest the same elimination techniques, but unfortunately he had attended a school where there was very little communication between teachers and parents.

As has been stated previously, all the adults in a handicapped child's life must be in agreement when trying to change negative or self-destructive behaviour; without the co-operation of everyone involved, any programme devised to help him will take a very long time to achieve successful results. Information gathering and discussion is an important part of any plan to modify a child's problematic behaviour. All the adults involved need to realise that it is vital to give him a balanced perception of human contact; all children need to feel secure within their environment and, for the multi-sensorily impaired child, this can often only be gained through calm, close bodily contact. People had become afraid of Thomas, so were withdrawing from him rather than drawing closer to him. The further away the adults withdrew, the more Thomas had had to display negative behaviour. The only person not afraid of him was his mother, which she had demonstrated by trying to restrain him from his dangerous and self-abusive actions.

I felt that we should help Thomas's mother to restructure her behaviour by helping her to observe him at a distance, and that we should demonstrate to Thomas that adults were not afraid of him and that he could find other ways of gaining our attention. By being able to 'stand back' from the problem, many parents can see other ways of solving the difficulties in discussion with their teacher or therapist.

I explained to Thomas's mother that we would initiate a programme to give Thomas as much loving bodily contact as possible, that we would only withdraw this contact if he began self-abusive behaviour, and that, as part of the programme, we would try to demonstrate to him that there were other legitimate means of using up his energies. A great many multiply handicapped children resort to rocking because they do not have the same outlets for their energy as their sighted hearing peers: rather than walk around the room, they will twirl on one spot; rather than run, they will stand and rock backwards and forwards in what appears to be a frenzied manner; and they will poke their eyes, bang their heads or bite themselves in order to gain stimulation from their bodies, which they would otherwise gain from their environment. Only by incorporating a set of structured play and work activities into the child's programme can we expect to have complete success. We cannot eliminate negative behaviour, mannerisms and blindisms, if the child has no legitimate activities with which to replace them.

Thomas's mother agreed to these ideas and also agreed that we should set ourselves a goal for each week, as well as the long-term goal of completely changing Thomas's behaviour within a year from the date of her first contact. If we do not set ourselves short-term goals and aim for a time-limited programme, the parents may not see that, with their co-operation, the behaviour which their child manifests is capable of being altered. But the time-limit must be a realistic one.

Thomas's Programme

1 *Rocking.* Thomas needed an outlet for his energies so we felt that, at first, we should join him in his rocking activity. As rocking often led to head-banging, we would not provide Thomas with a mattress to sit on, but would instead place a blanket on the floor for the rocking activity. We were fortunate in having contact with a musician who would help us to devise appropriate musical activities that we hoped would change Thomas's negative rocking behaviour into positive co-operative two-way interaction. The idea was that we would sing to Thomas as he rocked and, if he would allow this, we should hold hands and move together with the music. The musician was seated in a corner of the room; his role was clearly defined as being the provider of musical accompaniments, and he would not speak or take an active role in the sessions.

On entering the playroom on his first day, Thomas was greeted by soothing guitar music. The blinds of the playroom were closed and the room was lit by diffuse wall lighting. The only place which was well lit was the 'rocking blanket' on which the teacher sat. Thomas was led into the playroom by another teacher who then withdrew with Thomas's mother. We had already arranged that the rocking session would last for as long as Thomas's interest was sustained, and that his teacher would only withdraw close contact if he was self-abusive. The contact would not be withdrawn if he was abusive towards the teacher, because we were trying to establish that an important relationship was being formed. Week by week, through these intensive play sessions, Thomas began to appreciate that the adult was always there, would always remain calm and would always stay close and, gradually, he began to nestle up to the teacher and join her in singing games.

2 *Head-banging.* Thomas had managed to gain so much attention from head-banging that we felt that, whatever happened, we should never give him attention for this behaviour, and that we would not try to prevent him from banging his head. His mother had at one time been issued with a crash helmet (such as is sometimes used for epileptic children to prevent them from damaging their skulls), and she reported that when he wore the helmet, it had increased his behaviour problem. Once, he had smashed his head against a window, thus causing a great deal of damage and consequent attention. I advised her against using the crash helmet and agreed with her that it was reinforcing the negative activity. Careful observation of Thomas's head-banging led everyone to conclude that, in fact, he would often stop momentarily before or after banging his head, in order to discover what the adults' reactions were going to be. We felt that it should be clear to Thomas that he would receive a great deal of attention throughout all of his structured play sessions, but that he would receive no attention for ten seconds if he banged his head.

It is extremely important, when decisions are made about 'ignoring' negative behaviour, that it is absolutely clear to the child that approval has been withdrawn. Withdrawing approval for long periods of time can only lead him to conclude that he has to resort to even more bizarre and disturbing activity in order to win back the adult's attention. If a child has impaired sight and hearing, he cannot be reasoned with in the same way as a non-handicapped child, for reasoning requires language. The behaviour that is disapproved of must be clear to the child as well as to the adult, and the message concerning the withdrawal of approval must be equally clear. We decided that, if Thomas banged his head to gain attention, the teacher would put his hand on the part of his head which had been banged and would then take that hand and sign and say a very clear 'no'. They would both then sit still *together* for a period of ten seconds. Thomas soon learned that it was far more interesting to take part in other activities (and indeed rather boring to sit still for ten seconds), and his head-banging gradually decreased.

3 *Eye-poking.* It was easy for us to provide diffuse lighting in the playroom so as to reduce the opportunities for eye-poking to gain extra stimulation from a bright light source, but much more difficult to modify this long-term activity. We instituted exactly the same elimination techniques as those which we had initiated for James. Most children who become absorbed in self-stimulatory activity are in fact applying cause-and-effect principles, but they are manipulating their bodies to create an effect within the environment, rather than toys and activities.

Generally speaking, children tend to revert to their previous negative behaviour when under stress. It is therefore vital for parents and teachers to inform each other about occasions when negative behaviour is likely to recur. Without this co-operation complete elimination may not be possible.

Thomas was provided with some large pieces of equipment for use at home, so that his mother could be asked to remove the mattresses from his bedroom. He was given a rocking

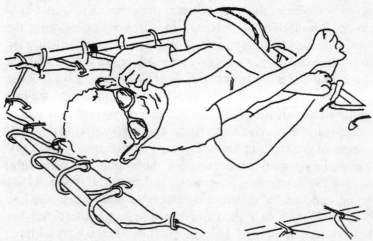

Thomas would not be allowed to use his trampoline if he reverted to his negative behaviour.

horse, a trampoline, a hopper (bouncing ball) and a swing, thus giving him legitimate outlets for his energy and channelling his rocking activity into more positive pastimes. First of all, he had to learn that he would not be allowed to indulge in any of his previous rocking, banging or eye-poking behaviour while using this new equipment. As soon as he attempted to exhibit any of his previous behaviour he was quietly removed for a period of ten seconds. We never increased the 'time out' from any activity, because we wanted it to be clear to Thomas that this was a temporary removal and we felt that he needed a clear message that it was his behaviour that was disapproved of and not he himself.

Daisy

Daisy was five years old at the time of referral. Like the two previous children, she had become so obsessed by light that she was having to resort to extreme measures in order to be close to the light source. Although she was so young she was extremely strong and would throw herself backwards and butt her head on an adult's body if she was restrained from going near the window, her favourite source of light. When possible, she would find the nearest piece of furniture in order to climb up to be closer to the light; when in the garden she would hold on to the clothes prop to try to climb up it towards the sunlight; she would take off her glasses and reverse them, then hold them up to her eyes so as to reflect the sun's rays into them. She had pulled out handfuls of hair from the back of her head and her face and body were bruised from where she had punched herself when she was prevented from light-gazing.

Daisy lived in a children's home and was subject to different means of controlling her behaviour. Sometimes she was disciplined extremely firmly and had been smacked on several occasions; sometimes she was inadvertently rewarded by being cuddled by different members of staff when she had bruised herself or pulled out her hair; and sometimes her behaviour was ignored, because the staff were so busy with the other children that they were unable to keep her under close observation all the time.

The interesting fact is that Daisy was not referred because of her extreme obsession with light, but because she had started smearing faeces both at night and during the daytime, and the staff felt they were unable to cope with this new problem. All her previous behaviour and the new problem were inter-related, and in fact the smearing proved to be much more simple to deal with than the staff at the children's home had envisaged, simply because it was new to Daisy. Old, en-trenched negative activity is very difficult to reduce, whereas new, less well-established habits can be remedied fairly quick-ly. Many children smear because they are trying to let people

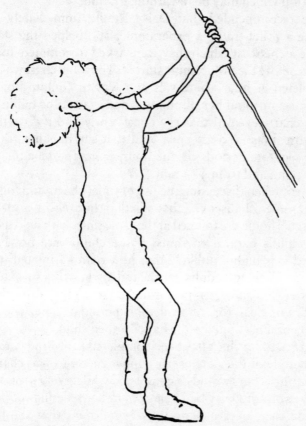

Daisy would hold on to the clothes prop to try to climb up it towards the sunlight.

know that they are ready to be completely toilet-trained and that they are trying to remove something which they find uncomfortable or offensive. Blind children cannot see the result of the smearing, but they can hear the reactions of other people to their activity. If the mess is very quietly removed with no comment *the first time it happens*, and if the child is seen to be ready to be toilet-trained, it is unlikely that the problem will occur again. If, however, a great deal of activity occurs, such as grumbling, smacking the child, fuss about changing the sheets or the child's clothes, then the child will realise that this exercise is worth repeating because he has gained so much attention which may be rewarding for him.

We recommended that Daisy should immediately commence a toilet-training programme, and helped the staff to devise a checklist which they were asked to complete for two weeks before the programme started. The toilet chart was to be completed at hourly intervals and was to contain objective information about her elimination and evacuation habits. Her toilet chart revealed that she consistently had a dirty nappy after breakfast and after tea, and that she remained dry for three separate periods of one hour, from 10–11 a.m., from 12–1 p.m., and from 3–4 p.m.

Often, when discussing the use of toilet charts and toileting programmes, I discover that all the children in a class or children's home are toileted at the same time, with no regard to each child's natural rhythms. If the child were not handicapped it is highly unlikely that he would be treated in this way. Children and adults use the toilet when they need to and not after they have just performed or when they are going to stay dry or clean for a considerable period of time. The same treatment must apply to the handicapped child.

Daisy's toilet chart has been completed for Monday to give an example of the state of her nappy when this was changed. This type of chart would be completed while trying to establish whether or not Daisy had a pattern to her toileting routine. It became clear over a period of several days that she had a pattern, that she was ready to be toilet trained and that it was apparent when would be the best time to sit her on the potty or

DAISY'S TOILET CHART

(Urinates) P.1
(Stools) P.2

Wet
Dry
Soiled
No

	7 am	8 am	9 am	10 am	11 am	12 am	1 pm	2 pm	3 pm	4 pm	5 pm	6 pm	7 pm
Mon	Wet	Wet Soiled	Wet	Dry	Wet	Dry	Wet	Wet	Dry	Wet	Wet Soiled	Dry	In Bed
Tues													
Wed													
Thur													
Fri													
Sat	Wet No	Wet P.2	Wet No	Dry No	Dry P.1	Dry P.1	Wet No	Dry P.1	Dry No	Wet P.1	Wet P.2	Dry P.1	In Bed
Sun													

toilet. Daisy's toilet chart has been completed for Saturday and here we see that she has begun to perform on the toilet. The important point to notice is that she is still in nappies, so the state of her nappies is recorded as wet or dry and her performance is also noted.

Daisy had been given far too many opportunities for smearing by the staff in the children's home, and they agreed with us that if she learned to use the toilet, these opportunities would be reduced. We observed her during a smearing occasion and realised that she was not really aware of the results of the activity and that she was light-gazing while unconsciously trying to remove the faeces and her soiled nappy. Once the staff began to toilet Daisy at her appropriate times she became more comfortable, and we were then able to tackle the real problem of her obsession with light in the same ways that we had used with James and Thomas. We gave her substitutes for her negative behaviour, one-to-one close physical contact, a structured programme based on observations of her needs and time to re-establish a perception of herself and her relationships with other people.

The multiply handicapped child with behaviour problems, which have resulted in him withdrawing from the world, needs to be gradually and firmly brought back into it and shown that it is more fun to be *with* people than without them.

10 Extending the Child's Skills

Careful assessment of the child's skills will enable the parent or teacher to extend each area of development, using their knowledge of him and his interests and bearing in mind his sight, hearing or physical impairments. It is often useful to write down the developmental goals which each child needs to consolidate or extend and to give a time limit for the achievement of these skills. For example:

Name   *Date*

Goal   *To be achieved by:*
                                              (date)

This record sheet will then provide a basis for much of the activity which is provided for the child throughout his daily plan. For example:

Name   *Date*
Emma   January 1986
Goal
Motor Skills
1 Emma needs to roll over by herself   date achieved
2 Emma needs to hold her head up for
   periods of up to five minutes   date achieved
3 Emma needs to sit unsupported   date achieved
Visual Skills
1 Emma needs to track
   a moving light   date achieved

Each record sheet should give observational and objective guidelines for achievements which are within the realistic capabilities of each child. It is always a good idea to include skills from each developmental area and not to concentrate on one particular area, such as vision or auditory training. The handicapped child is a whole child and has the same global needs for social and emotional development as the non-handicapped child; the record sheet should be used as a guideline for the achievement of skills but should never be thought of as a rigid, inflexible plan which has to be followed at all costs. It must always be borne in mind that children will learn best when all the activities presented to them are fun, and a high element of enjoyment will enable the child to move on from one skill area to another with greater facility.

USEFUL REFERENCE BOOK
Children's Developmental Progress by Mary D. Sheridan. Windsor: NFER/Nelson, 1978.

Visual Development

Unless the child is totally blind, we can say that most children will benefit from some form of visual training, but this will depend to a large extent on your knowledge and understanding of the implications of your child's eye condition. Space does not allow for detailed discussion of all the possible eye conditions which multiply handicapped or deaf-blind children may have.

Doreen Norris writes:

Many deaf-blind children have useful residual vision, and vision is often the sensory channel they prefer. Some of these children, however, especially those who are more severely multiply handicapped, will experience difficulties in using their limited sight to maximum effect.

It is possible to plan a programme of visual training that will help deaf-blind children to increase their visual competence and, as use of vision plays such a major role in the early development of the child, indirectly to facilitate their all-round development. An understanding of the difficulties the children face in using their limited vision, a careful assessment of what visual skills they have and what skills they can, or need to, develop, will provide a base from which to plan such a programme.

Understanding the Problem

The way in which deaf-blind children use their residual vision is highly individualised and not always determined solely by the degree of visual impairment. It is important that the person planning the programme has an awareness of the possible problems facing the child, in order to structure the programme appropriately and make modifications should the need arise.

Delayed Motor Development

It has already been stated that vision plays a major role in early infant development and this is particularly true of early motor development. Visual stimulation is an important factor in motivating the child to lift his head, crawl, walk, etc., and consequently, with restricted vision he is likely to spend longer lying down, in a position where there is usually little to look at and where it is difficult to practise using a variety of visual/motor skills.

If the deaf-blind child has not yet achieved good head control and/or good sitting balance, these factors, too, must be considered when planning the setting for the training programme.

Fragmented Visual Information

With incomplete visual information it is more difficult to make sense of what is seen or to select significant factors from the environment. Consequently, the deaf-blind child is less likely to pay visual attention to the world around him. It takes longer to gather information and perceptual distortions can easily arise. Again, the adult should be aware of these factors and aim to minimise the effects by presenting materials clearly, pacing the training appropriately or repeating the experience as often as is necessary.

Impaired Hearing

Remember also that the deaf-blind child is experiencing similar problems in using his other distance sense. While he is likely to use his impaired sight in preference to his impaired hearing, there will be an absence of formal language which could otherwise be used to direct his use of vision or correct distorted perceptions. It is unlikely at an early stage of development that limited auditory information can be used to supplement and/ or integrate visual information without the direct help of an adult.

Specific Eye Conditions

Some eye conditions present their own specific problems and influence the way in which a child can use what sight he has. It is therefore important to be aware of your child's eye condition so that realistic goals can be set and procedures structured to minimise the effect.

Additional Handicapping Conditions

In planning a programme of visual training for the deaf-blind child the adult needs to consider any additional disabilities which add another dimension to the child's already complex problem. For example, a child with epilepsy may be experiencing small 'absences' which make a planned exercise meaningless, and the adult needs to observe the child closely in case this is so. A change of setting, materials used or time of day selected for training may help to overcome this problem. A physical handicap or varying degrees of intellectual impairment must also influence the way the programme is structured.

Since deaf-blind children have to work harder for less, it is not surprising that they are often visually distractable and inattentive. Neither can it be assumed that without the direct intervention of the adult they will use their limited sight effectively. The more complex their handicaps, the more dependent they are on a well planned programme.

Assessing Functional use of Vision

Before embarking on a programme of visual training it is necessary to gather together the following information:

—how children use what vision they have;
—what visual motor/perceptual skills they have already acquired;
—medical and ophthalmological information.

Information gathered in this way should then form the base from which the programme of visual training is started. However, the process of assessment must be ongoing so that the programme can be monitored and developed.

1 *Use of Vision*. It is necessary to find out how the deaf-blind child uses what vision he has by observing him closely at different times of day, using a range of toys and everyday objects. Observations can be carried out over a number of days and factors such as lighting, colour, size and pattern of objects should all be considered. It is important to observe very carefully and to record observations, as changes in behaviour may be slight or easily misinterpreted.

2 *Visual Motor/Perceptual Skills*. These skills develop sequentially and have been detailed in a number of developmental checklists. Compare the child's present level of visual functioning against such a scale to help determine, a) what the child can already do, b) what the next teaching goal might be, and c) what 'gaps' there might be in his development.

3 *Medical and Ophthalmological Information*. It is helpful to have as much information as possible about the deaf-blind child's eye condition, his general health and other medical information, as all these factors will influence the way you plan the programme of visual training.

Planning the Programme

The new-born baby quickly adapts to using his sight. The non-handicapped infant's visual competence develops rapidly, via a hierarchy of motor and perceptual skills which are acquired by his constant interactions with an ever-widening environment. An emerging skill, which at first appears to be quite 'clumsy' and inconsistent, is soon refined by repeated practice.

In the deaf-blind child this process is severely limited and/or interrupted. The programme of visual training should aim to assist the efficient use of what vision the child has. The suggestions for training given below are only some of the ways in which these skills can be encouraged.

Guidelines
The following guidelines can apply to all levels of training, having regard to how the child is functioning at present.

1   Start with large objects and reduce size as child becomes more skilled.

2   Start with intense stimulation (as with use of light in a darkened room). Work towards more normal levels of contrast.

3   Start with toys or objects that the child will most readily look at and slowly modify colour, pattern and shape to increase the range of objects that will arouse his interest.

4   Remember to work at the child's pace. At first it will take longer for him to transfer his gaze from one object to another, or follow a moving toy, but as he becomes more skilled, with practice, the pace can be increased.

5   Keep intensive training to short but frequent (once or twice a day) and regular periods.

6   Give the child time to master and consolidate a skill before moving on to a higher level of skill. Vary materials used if interest flags.

7   Show the child how to perform a skill such as tracking, by physically assisting if necessary—then gradually reduce the level of support given.

8   Encourage the child's efforts in whatever way is appropriate or most effective, but remember that eventually using his sight well will be its own reward. Selection of materials, seating, settling, etc., play an important role in gaining and maintaining his interest and co-operation.

9   Cut out other visual distractions as far as possible, at least initially, so that the task is made visually clear.

10   Set clear, short-term objectives and record progress.

11   Remember that opportunities for using vision occur

throughout the day; whenever possible the child should be encouraged to practise using the skills he has learnt.

Visual Awareness and Attention

Encourage the child to become visually aware and attentive to visual stimulation in his immediate environment.

—Place him near a light source; perhaps a coloured lamp, or in sunlight (not shining into his eyes) while he is lying or sitting.

—Hang bright or shiny toys/objects that reflect light (mirror, rattle) or move easily (strips of foil wrapping paper) where they will catch the light from a window or lamp. Remember to place the toys near the child, within a short focal length and where he may involuntarily touch them.

—Change lighting conditions to attract attention.

The adult's role is to observe the child's reactions carefully and to select and place appropriate materials. Encourage an observed reaction to the visual stimulus by perhaps repeating the experience—moving a toy, turning a light on and off or taking his hand towards a toy.

Although the child can be exposed to such stimulation in the absence of the adult, it is important to spend short periods playing with him in these conditions so that his responses may be helped to become more positive and consistent, and favoured toys and objects can be selected for further training.

Fixation

A more sustained and consistent response to a visual stimulus is now sought and turning towards the stimulus encouraged.

—Use a coloured torch, or 'Glow Worm', in a darkened room; switch the torch on to one side, then the other.

—Dangle a shiny toy or paper at the optimum focal length until he fixates on the toy, then move it to another position.

—Encourage child to look towards your face, perhaps by wearing a 'Disco hat'.

—Experiment with toys of varied bright colours or patterns.

Tracking

The child is now asked to follow a moving object. Begin by working at eye level at optimum focal length, and work towards watching the toy moving across a table or on the floor.

—Use a coloured or shaded torch, move from midline to left or right. Then move the torch slowly from left to right, gradually extending to moving a light through 180°, then vertically and diagonally.

At first it may be necessary to move the light very slowly, keeping the child's visual attention as the light is moved, but with practice it should be possible to make the following action smoother and quicker.

—Dangle a bright toy across the child's line of vision, left-right, up and down. Do not discourage the child from reaching out to touch the toy.

—Roll a ball slowly across the table, or use a clockwork toy or car.

—Play with bubbles.

—Look for toys that develop tracking, e.g. Sigzag or tumbling clown.

—Bounce 'power' balls when the child becomes really skilled.

Convergence Training

The aim here is to help the child to focus on an object as it approaches and moves away.

—Use a shaded torch or bright object and move it very slowly towards the child to the point where the child no longer follows it, then move slowly away; bring the object gradually closer and closer to his face (about 10 cm or 4 ins) before moving away.

Accommodation

The aim of this training is to help the child to focus on objects at varying distances from his eyes. At first all training exercises are presented at the child's optimum focal length, but he is then encouraged to extend the distance at which he will regard an object. There are plenty of opportunities to develop this skill throughout the day. Practise this skill by:

—Shining a (coloured) torch on a table near the child. Switch it off and shine it in a different place; make it more exciting by changing the colour.

—Placing a brightly coloured or shiny toy near the child. Move it further away, to left or right.

—Putting a favourite toy near the child, and another further away.

Eye Contact

1　Eye-to-eye contact. For a deaf-blind child with some useful vision this skill should be encouraged, as it can then play an important part in developing relationships and communication skills. Eye-to-eye contact can be encouraged in many playful situations, e.g. playing 'peep-bo', wearing a zany hat, or varying the angle at which you look at the child.

If eye-to-eye contact is very difficult to achieve, hold something the child likes (a toy, or a crisp) in front of your eyes, with the child sitting opposite. Give him the object as a reward if he looks at you. At first reward for a fleeting glance, but gradually expect more sustained eye contact.

2　Eye/object contact. This is a prerequisite for developing hand and eye co-ordination and visual perception skills. Encourage the development of this skill by:

—Making sure the child looks at all objects before giving him the offered object.

—Choosing favourite toys or objects, and holding them within the child's reach, only releasing them to the child when he looks at the toy, and gradually extending the length of time you ask the child to look at the toy before giving it to him.

Hand and Eye Co-ordination

The refinement of this skill is dependent upon the child's increasing manipulative skill. However, it can be encouraged from an early stage as the child reaches out to touch a toy. If the child is looking towards a toy but making no attempt to touch it, take his hand and place it over the toy.

—At first hold a toy where the child can reach easily and make sure the toy is visually exciting. Give as much help as necessary to begin with, gradually reducing the level of help as the child becomes more practised.

Extend the skills by asking the child to:

—pick up toys from the table, take rings off a stick, etc;
—take objects out of a box or bowl;
—put objects into a box;
—post objects through a single hole;
—put small objects (beads, pegs) into a plastic bottle.

Scanning

This is the ability to search visually for an object and a skill which the normal baby gradually develops. For the deaf-blind child with only limited sight (and no recognised sound cues to help him) this may prove a particularly difficult skill to acquire and, again, can be encouraged in everyday routines.

—Play searching games: for a favourite toy, on the table, on the floor.
—'Hide' a favourite toy among other toys on the table.
—Roll a ball down a tube.
—Drop a toy on the floor and encourage the child to search.

Conclusion

Deaf-blind children can benefit enormously from using their residual vision but, as in other areas, these skills have to be taught if they are to use this sight effectively. Whilst everyday routines and activities give excellent opportunities for practising using vision, there is also a place for intensive structured training which would be considered the norm in encouraging the development of other motor abilities. Well-developed visual motor skills will then provide a base for an ongoing programme of perceptual training.

Three excellent books recommended for further reference on this subject are:

A Vision Guide for Teachers of Deaf-Blind Children by Marvin Efron and Beth Reilly DuBoff. Raleigh: North Carolina Department of Public Instruction, 1976.

Visual Disorders in the Handicapped Child by John L. Goble. New York: Marcel Dekker, Inc., 1984.
Visual Handicap in Children, edited by Vernon Smith and John Keen. Spastics International Medical Publications, 1979.

A pamphlet full of useful ideas is:
Guidelines for Teachers and Parents of Visually Handicapped Children with Additional Handicaps. The Royal National Institute for the Blind, 224-6-8 Great Portland Street, London W1N 6AA.

The importance of utilising the child's visual skills is heightened when considering his fine motor/perceptual skills. The multiply handicapped child's limited sight will monitor his grasp and much of his learning will be governed by whether or not he is using the sight that he has. Often teachers and parents are interested in the diagnosis of the eye condition, but in fact it is the way in which the child uses his sight that is more important, and the same eye condition can result in completely different usage depending on the character of the child, the experiences to which he has been exposed and his other handicapping conditions which may limit or extend his abilities to use his vision.

As an example, we can look at the skill of grasping. Some children are able to grasp but will not look at what is grasped, or they will reach for an object but overshoot it and be unable to grasp; others will be able to look at a proffered object but will need co-active help in stretching for it in order to be able to grasp it; yet others will look and search for an object that is meaningful to them (such as sweets) but will not look and search for objects that they find less motivating. Some children will manipulate objects when they are put in their hands directly, but need encouragement to transfer objects from one hand to another because they appear not to be aware of one half of their bodies.

All children have an optimum focal length and it is common for some children to lose contact with an object, so that they will need training to help them keep it within their range of vision. Tracking exercises to follow an object are often the beginning of visual awareness in some children, and a coloured light may usefully be employed in the tracking exercises. Children need to be able to track from midline to the side and back again, from midline upwards, from midline downwards, from midline and then from side to side, from each side of the body to the other horizontally, to track up and down and then to track diagonally. Tracking can lead the children towards being able to focus at different distances and then to reach forward beyond their immediate grasp for the object with which they are presented.

All information which can help the teacher or parent to help the child to function at his optimum capacity is useful: for instance, does a particular colour attract the child? Does he see better in certain light? Can he see all around him? Does his colour vision appear to be normal? Does he need to move objects so as to get a clearer picture of them? Does he need to view objects at a particular angle, or can he sit upright in order to see clearly? Is he photophobic?

Multiply handicapped children have normal needs and, as has been stated elsewhere, we should help them to follow these normal sequences as far as possible. But when considering the visual abilities of our children we have heightened awareness of their needs and will have to adopt a different approach or methods to help the child to achieve necessary skills. In vision and in hearing skills we *see* the difference between the sighted hearing child and the deaf-blind or multiply handicapped child, because all his learning is going to be affected by his ability to compensate for his lack of sight and hearing, or his physical disability.

A very useful resource guide for teachers working with visually handicapped children is *Concept Development for Visually Handicapped Children* by William T. Lydon and M. Loretta McGraw. New York: The American Foundation for the Blind, Inc., 1982. Also recommended as further reading is a very practical book, *Blindness and Partial Sight* by Astrid Klemz. Cambridge: Woodhead-Faulkner, 1977.

Articles and assessment schedules relevant to the assessment of vision in the severely multiply handicapped child.

A Vision Guide for Teachers of Deaf-Blind Children by Marvin Efron and Beth Reilly DuBoff. (See p. 214.)

Manual for the Assessment of a Deaf-Blind Multiply Handicapped Child by J. M. Rudolph and B. J. Collins. Michigan: Mid-West Regional Center for Services to Deaf-Blind, 1975.

The Next Step on the Ladder by G. B. Simon. Wolverhampton: British Institute of Mental Handicap, 1981.

Auditory Development

The educational implications of a hearing loss have been described in a highly recommended book, *The Hearing Impaired Child and the Family* by Michael Nolan and Ivan G. Tucker. London: Souvenir Press, Second edition 1986.

It is self evident that although all children are born with a capacity to communicate, the deaf child will, if he has an additional handicap, need someone else to help him to perceive that his efforts to communicate are being received. Adults must create a framework for his learning by giving him early linguistic experience which will often be entirely dependent on gestures and the interchange of gestures. If we observe the young child we shall see that this is not so 'abnormal' as sometimes appears. Sign language comes before verbal language. The interchange of a mother saying goodbye to her child will often be enhanced by the fact that her baby will wave 'bye bye' long before he can speak. The child's understanding of his environment and his situation is vital; the adult must interpret for the child until he is sure the child has the inner language to interpret his environment for himself.

The non-handicapped sighted hearing child learns globally, and the same is true for the deaf-blind child. For instance, when a young child is taken several times a day into the bathroom to wash his hands and dry them, he will understand from tactual, visual and auditory clues, and from the whole situation, that what he is expected to do is dry his hands on a towel; he probably hears, 'Now, let's dry our hands,' he sees the towel and he feels it as he dries himself. All this information can be given to the deaf-blind or multiply handicapped child, but we need to take a longer time to ensure that he has understood the situation. He will need verbal cues, signed cues, tactual cues, visual cues, and occasionally olfactory cues to give him complete understanding of the situation.

When we consider a hearing loss it is useful to think of what the sighted deaf child will need to compensate for his lack of hearing. If he needs to have a compensatory environment and special teaching facilities, these will be absolutely essential for the deaf-blind or multiply handicapped child. Communication is the key to all further learning, and the extension of skills in all areas will depend on the child's ability to interact with other people. The deaf-blind child may have a mixture of conductive and sensori-neural deafness (conductive deafness is often commonly associated with problems in the functioning of the middle ear). Once these problems have cleared up either spontaneously, through medication or through minor surgery, the problem may be completely alleviated or, unfortunately, it may recur.

Middle ear problems sometimes go unnoticed in the multiply handicapped child as he has so many major difficulties to cope with, but even a minor loss of hearing can affect the lifestyle and the understanding of a blind child, so this should always be looked for when assessing our children. Unfortunately sensori-neural deafness is not able to be treated medically and is a permanent condition.

Children who have sensori-neural loss will be able to be fitted with hearing aids. Nowadays many children are issued with radio aids which enable the parent or other adult to communicate much more directly with the child than the standard post-aural (behind the ear) or body-worn aid. The care of hearing aids is very well documented in *The Hearing Impaired Child and the Family* by Michael Nolan and Ivan G. Tucker (see p. 217), and cannot be stressed too highly. The care of the hearing aid is almost as important as the hearing aid itself, for if the aid does not function properly and gives

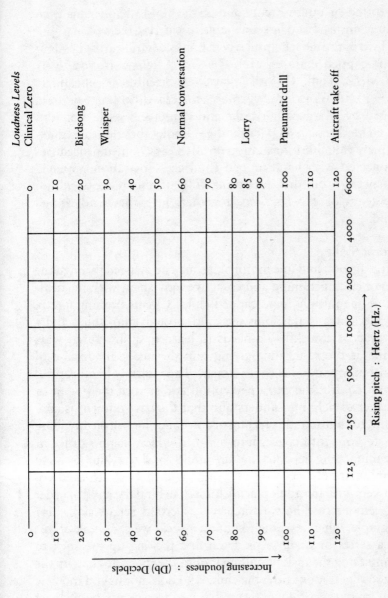

An audiogram shows the level of loudness at which the child hears but obviously cannot show the use to which he puts his hearing.

distorted or intermittent sounds, the child will become even more confused and less amenable to wearing the aid.

Two of the most helpful recent books describing the needs of handicapped children are: *The Child with a Handicap* by D. M. B. Hall. Oxford: Blackwell Scientific Publications, 1984; and *Working Together with Handicapped Children*, edited by Margaret Griffiths and Philippa Russell. London: Souvenir Press, 1985. Both these books, besides giving extremely valuable information on all the assessment procedures connected with handicapped children, show an enlightened perspective on the important role of the parents within the team of experts who, together, help the handicapped child.

Motor Skills

Large (gross) and fine motor skills may be assisted through the use of circuit training and co-active movement with the deaf-blind or multiply handicapped child. Circuit training (see p. 117) is a means of helping the child through enjoyable activity to practise the skills he needs to learn in a structured way, while at the same time giving him the necessary feeling of constancy within his environment. The multiply handicapped child requires the extra perception and skill of the parent or teacher to help him understand that the environment is constant, for without this feeling of constancy he will be unwilling to step out into space, into a world which has no order or meaning. He depends on an adult to show him how to manipulate objects, and often this will be best achieved co-actively with the adult placing himself behind the child in order to demonstrate how to achieve a certain set of skills: for example, when learning to put on a sock, we can think of this as a series of small steps, from first picking up the sock to completing the task of pulling it onto the foot and then up the leg so that it looks tidy; the child who does not have a motoric pattern of this skill will be unable even to pick up the sock, let alone complete the series of complicated fine finger and hand movements to enable him to pull the sock up his leg.

Some people find it useful to write down all the steps in a

The adult guides the child, hand over hand, to complete the task . . . She is then **encouraged to transfer** these skills onto another task.

given task so that they can decide whether or not an individual child can learn the task through 'backward chaining' or 'forward chaining'. Some children may find it easier to complete a task and others may find it easier to start the task. There is no definitive answer to the question of how we should approach our children—all of them are individual, therefore all should have individual approaches and individual programmes and, within these, the approach and the programme should alter as the child grows in ability and skill. With each child we need to follow five rules which will govern our behaviour before deciding on the way in which a particular child will learn a specific skill. These rules are:

1   to know the child;
2   to identify the child's abilities;
3   to identify the child's needs;
4   to observe the child and the way he solves problems;
5   to identify the task which the child is expected to learn and to decide whether or not this task is relevant to the child and his needs.

If we follow these rules, occasionally we shall find that what we thought we wanted the child to achieve is in fact slightly different from the goal we originally set. For example, we may have decided that the child needs to self feed, but applying the rules to a particular child may help us to discover that what he needs before self-feeding is to be able to hold his head, body, hands or arms in a particular fashion; or we may have decided that the child should spoon-feed, but then, having observed him, we may feel that it is extremely important for him to finger-feed because of his tactile needs as a blind or multiply handicapped child. Constant observation of our children will prevent us from making assumptions about their disabilities and our abilities to teach them! Three invaluable books on the subject of motor development are:
Handling the Young Cerebral Palsied Child at Home by N. R. Finnie. London: Heinemann Medical Books, 1978.
The Wheelchair Child by Philippa Russell. London: Souvenir Press, Second edition 1984.

'Stimulation of movement: a review of modern therapeutic techniques' in *Movement and Child Development* by K. Holt. London: Heinemann Medical Books, 1975.

Behaviour and Emotional Development

Children learn by doing. If they are encouraged to do things for themselves, to learn to enjoy skills that lead them towards independence, their social and emotional development is bound to keep pace with their growing needs and awareness. Sometimes adaptations to our methods of teaching will be necessary—perhaps the environment will need modifications, or the toys we provide will have to be more carefully chosen, or the means of communication we use will be slightly different from those we would use with a sighted hearing child; but our whole behaviour towards each child will be helping him to reach out towards his own personal goals. Extending these goals will depend to a large extent on his visual, auditory, tactile and mobility skills and, within these developmental areas, we shall have to have reinforced, through strong communication signals, our desire to teach him or his desire to learn.

Remember: co-act; react; interact.

When we co-act with the child we must be open to his signals and should not expect him to receive our attempts to communicate unless we are prepared to react to his signals. Once we have reacted to him, then interaction between child and adult will be possible. Interaction is dependent in the beginning on close physical contact, but this can gradually be withdrawn once the child has absolute certainty about himself, his environment and what is expected of him within that environment.

Two practical books that would assist anyone wishing to devise clear developmental programmes for the handicapped child in their care are: *Getting Through to your Handicapped Child* by Elizabeth Newson and Tony Hipgrave. Cambridge: Cambridge University Press, 1983; and *The Next Step on the Ladder* by G. B. Simon (see p. 217).

In the world of the deaf-blind or multiply handicapped

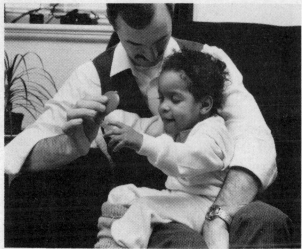

The adult extends the child's range of skills by encouraging her to move the object in a variety of ways.

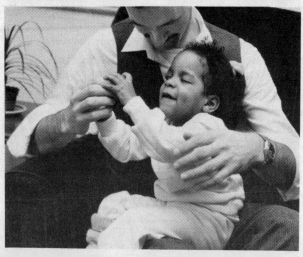

child, nothing can be left to chance; and yet, of course, we can still have a great deal of fun, enjoyment, pleasure and satisfaction from working with our children. Two books that are an important addition to this subject are: *Toys and Playthings in Development and Remediation* by John and Elizabeth Newson. London: George Allen & Unwin, 1979; and *Toys and Play for the Handicapped Child* by Barbara Riddick. London: Croom Helm, 1982.

Sometimes parents must feel overwhelmed by a sense of urgency when considering the needs of their handicapped child. However, it is still possible to relax and have fun with the most severely handicapped child. When looked at objectively, some tasks seem quite boring and repetitive, but there are many ways of turning certain skill areas into games. For example, Lauren needs to learn paper folding, which is something within her capabilities; initially she will need lots of help and demonstration from her parents, but later she can move on to doing this in imitation. She could either paper-fold in isolation or it could be linked to drawing by getting her to 'write a letter first', and then folding her letter and posting it through a slit in a cardboard box. Her parents will remember to make the slit small enough for the 'letter' to require folding a few times before it will fit. Another game that Lauren's parents have played with their little girl to improve the use of her distance vision is to take articles which they know she can identify by signing, and hide these in front of her; the articles were a spoon, a small ball, a little doll, her hairbrush, her glasses and her shoe. Each object was held up in front of Lauren, and she was asked to identify it through signing before it was hidden under a cloth. Lauren quickly learned to find the article under the cloth and then, using the same principle, her parents moved the objects and toys further away, which intrigued their daughter and provided a great deal of fun and laughter, although the aim of the game was quite serious: her distance vision was being utilised, her signing was being given practice and all the interactions between parent and child were reinforced.

Zachary is mobile and exploratory and now uses his partial

hearing to orientate and locate when he is in a known environment. His parents have been able to provide him with many hours of fun in the garden by relocating some of his outdoor play equipment. He has a swing at the end of the garden and, halfway up, is his rabbit hutch to which he journeys twice daily to feed his pet rabbits. Because of the space between the swing and the rabbit hutch Zachary had not been able to find his way between the two, so his parents moved them slightly closer together, and moved his slide to the top of the garden, thus creating a circuit which he will be able to remember as a mental map: slide, rabbit hutch, swing, and vice versa. Paying attention to small details and entering into the mind of the child will enable any parent to extend a child's skills in a variety of ways which need not be formalised or too closely structured.

Three books that describe the specialist needs of the deaf-blind child are:

Deaf-Blind Infants and Children: A Developmental Guide by John M. McInnes and Jacquelyn A. Treffrey. Milton Keynes: Open University Press, 1982.

Understanding the Deaf-Blind Child by Peggy Freeman. London: Heinemann, 1975.

The Deaf-Blind Baby by Peggy Freeman. London: Heinemann, 1985.

Toys and Play Aids

A good toy is one that can be used in a variety of ways. All the toys listed here have a cause-and-effect principle, so that if the child does something, then an effect will be produced. This should stimulate the child to repeat the action and so extend his play activity.

Abacus Balls	Escor
Activity Box	Playskool
Activity Centre	Fisher-Price
Animal Squeakers	Galt
Baby Action Ball	Playskool
Chatter Telephone	Fisher-Price
Chime Ball	Fisher-Price

Clatterpillar	Kiddicraft
Clic Clac Rattle	Kiddicraft
Coloured Patchwork Balls (set of 4)	ESA
Cradle Play	Kiddicraft
Drill Bells	Galt
Fighting Robot	Toy Aids
Flip Fingers	Kiddicraft
Flutterball	Playskool
Flying Saucer	Toy Aids
Hammer Balls	Galt
Happy Apple	Fisher-Price
Jack-in-the-Box	Fisher-Price
Jingle Bells	Galt
Leybourne Mirror Frame	Four to Eight
Leybourne Colour Frame	Four to Eight
Maracas	Galt
Music Box Radio	Fisher-Price
Music Box Record Player	Fisher-Price
Musical Rabbit	Kiddicraft
Novelty Tops	ESA
Nursery Trampoline	ESA and Galt
Plastic Slinky	ESA
Pop Up Men	Galt
Pull a Tune Bluebird	Fisher-Price
Rock a Stack	Fisher-Price
Safety Baby Walker	ESA
Tambourine	Galt and others
Turn and Learn Activity Centre	Fisher-Price

As far as possible, all toys should be chosen with the special needs of the child in mind, with the thought that play should always be fun and that, unless the toy is designed for two or more people, the child should quickly be able to learn to activate or manipulate it for himself once he has been shown co-actively. It is also important to remember that we are thinking about toys and play aids and not in terms of what are sometimes described as 'educational toys'. In other words, the toys are for home use or for those moments in school when children are given the opportunity to play freely; no toys have been included that come into the range of specialist toys, designed to encourage olfactory skills, auditory skills, visual skills, tactile skills, but are listed here for the element of fun, enjoyment and pleasure that the child can gain from them.

Some toys and play aids can easily be made at home and could include:

1   *Feely Board*. This makes use of old socks, tights or pieces of material, in which are placed a variety of *safe* materials such as dried peas, wood blocks, corks. Each sock is filled with a different type of material, and the socks are then sewn separately and very firmly onto a board or large piece of material.

2   *Feely Bags*. Separate feely bags can be made in a variety of textures and can be kept in a large bag made from material which is the same as one of the small bags, or several of them, to add more interest.

3   *Feely Box*. Probably the most simple play aid to make. Fill a cardboard box with all types of paper for the child to sift through and sort, or put in the box a lot of wooden spoons, saucepan lids and other interesting *safe* pieces of kitchen equipment for the child to explore.

4   *Feely Tights*. A pair of old tights with different kinds of paper pushed into them will make a very interesting first toy for a multiply handicapped child. Each leg of the tights can be placed on either side of the child, and the 'body' part then makes a very interesting cushion for his head if the tights are filled with newspaper. If the child is physically handicapped but able to move his head, the sensation of making an interesting noise with his head on this crushed paper is often extremely intriguing for the young multiply handicapped child.

5   *Wine Boxes* have within them a silver bag which contains the wine. Once the wine has been drunk, you are left with a very interesting bag which can be filled with a variety of *safe* materials such as water, lentils, rice.

6   *Tins.* All sorts and sizes of tins can be filled with different materials, particularly dried rice, macaroni or lentils, all of which make very satisfying sounds, as do dog chains and budgerigar toys.

7   *Jars, Pots and Pans* all provide experience of learning to twist, turn, take off lids and put them back on again. If a jar has a piece of food in it or a favourite toy, the ability to learn to twist and turn can be further encouraged. However, jars, pots and pans are usually used in the kitchen, as kitchen equipment, and it is important to emphasise to the child that these objects have other uses and are not *just toys*; with any multiply handicapped or deaf-blind child, we are trying to get the message clearly to them about the properties of objects, and sometimes it may not be desirable to give them 'real' things to play with in case they become muddled as to their usage.

8   *A Washing-up Bowl*, with sand or water in it and a few things to play with, can give the child a great deal of pleasure and amusement. If, as occasionally happens, the child does not like playing with sand, then feely pieces of material can be substituted, for example, split peas, macaroni, lentils, etc. There are also some children who do not like playing with water. This is not unusual and should never be forced on the child. Sometimes it is useful to put only a minute amount of water in the bottom of the washing-up bowl, and then to place in it a favourite toy which the child will reach for, getting his hands wet as he does so. This is one small way of encouraging him to get his hands wet. Gradually the water can be increased and the motivating toy can be exchanged for appropriate water-play toys.

9   *A Large Cardboard Box* can often make a wonderful environment for a young child or multiply handicapped child to experience. It is a safe place in which to play, with an environment that can be altered according to the child's mood and needs. Different materials can be provided to sit on in the box, such as an old towel or a blanket; one or two toys (one favourite toy, perhaps one new toy) can be given to the child to

play with; but most importantly, the box may give him a feeling of security because he can feel the edges of his environment all the time. (It must, however, be emphasised that no child should be introduced to a box, left in a box or even sat in a box if there is any thought that this will create fear. There should **never** be a lid on the box which the child could pull over himself). Once the child is mobile, a box is often not something that he will wish to sit in, and it should never be used as a playpen.

Songs to Sing Together
Five recommended books which contain a variety of action songs to sing together are:
Sociable Songs (set of four) by A. Mendoza. London: Oxford University Press, 1970.
The Goldie Leigh Song Book by S. Beresford Peirse, J. du Feu, J. Worthington and P. Nordoff. London: Goldie Leigh Hospital.
Apusskidu: 56 songs chosen for Children by P. Blakeley, D. Gadsby and B. Harrop. London: A. & C. Black.
Okki-Tokki-Unga: Action songs chosen for children by L. Friend, D. Gadsby and B. Harrop. London: A. & C. Black.
The Oxford Nursery Song Book. Oxford University Press, Third edition 1984.

Singing together can either be a purely pleasurable experience or it can be an aid to helping the child remember, recognise, discriminate and associate sounds with actions, actions with words, and words with meaning. Singing and music activities can be a great help in assisting the child to organise his hearing and to become aware of the 'sound-no sound' principle; through sharing with him singing, action games and music activities, it is possible to create opportunities for:
—listening out for a sound;
—anticipating a sound;
—and so on.
The child who is introduced very early to meaningless

auditory input, such as a constant radio or television, will very often cut out from sounds that mean nothing to him, and because of the background noise the world will appear to him to be a confusion of jumbled and chaotic noises. But the child who is introduced to the idea of listening, and the enjoyment of meaningful auditory input, will often learn to localise the sound source and learn to imitate sound patterns and rhythms; he will expect to listen.

As Paul Ennals says, it is not enough simply to *identify* a sound as, say, coming from a car. The child should also *interpret* the sound to discover that there is a road nearby, and *locate* the sound to know exactly where the road is. Each skill can be encouraged separately, but when you help one you are sure to be helping others. Practise the art of careful listening. If you sit quietly, how many different sounds can you hear which the child may be able to identify? All the sounds within his range of hearing will need explaining to him. You can experiment with making sounds together. You can collect a 'sound box' with jars and tins containing different things such as pebbles, rice, sand, buttons, bottle tops and sea shells, with which to make a variety of sounds. Collect small pieces of metal, wood, plastic, cardboard, paper, felt and other material and help him to find out how to make different noises by shaking, rubbing, banging, tapping and scratching them.

Listen together for cars, buses, lorries, vans, motorcycles, taxis and refuse lorries. Help him to interpret some of the sounds he hears by giving him practical experience, such as showing him the refuse collectors when they carry the rubbish away and put it in the refuse lorry, collecting the milk bottle from the milk float and watching/listening to the float as it drives away.

Helpful Organisations

The Royal National Institute for the Blind, 224 Great Portland Street, London W1. (Tel. 01-388 1266)

Royal National Institute for the Deaf, 105 Gower Street, London WC1. (Tel. 01-387 8033)

SENSE, The National Deaf-Blind and Rubella Association,

311 Gray's Inn Road, London WC1X 8PT (Tel. 01-278 1000)

Handbooks of Information
Help starts here (for parents of children with special needs)
Free from the Voluntary Council for Handicapped Children, National Children's Bureau, 8 Wakley Street, London EC1V 7QE. (Tel. 01-278 9441)
The Disability Rights Handbook
Published by the Disability Alliance Educational and Research Association, 25 Denmark Street, London WC2 8NJ. (Tel. 01-240 0806)

Toys and Play Aids Suppliers
Handicapped Persons Research Unit, Newcastle upon Tyne Polytechnic, 1 Coach Lane, Coach Lane Campus, Newcastle upon Tyne NE7 7TW. (Tel. 0632 664061)
PLAY MATTERS/The Toy Libraries Association for Handicapped Children, 68 Churchway, London NW1 1LT. (Tel. 01-387 9592)
Toy Aids Projects, Lodbourne Farmhouse, Lodbourne, Gillingham, Dorset SP8 4EH. (Tel. 07476 2256)

Books for Children
Having a Hearing Test by Althea. Dinosaur Publications. ISBN 0 85122 263 3.
Picture Books for Special Situations: *The Boy Who Couldn't Hear* by Freddy Bloom, *Ben* by Victoria Shennan, *Suzy* by Elizabeth Chapman, *Rachel* by Elizabeth Fanshawe (all published by the Bodley Head, London).
What's That? by Virginia Allen Jensen and Dorcas Woodbury Haller. Collins, Glasgow and London. ISBN 0 00 195910 7.

Equipment Catalogues
Paul and Marjorie Abbatt Ltd., PO Box 22, Harlow, Essex CM19 5AY.
Community Playthings, Robertsbridge, Sussex TN32 5DR.

Early Learning Centre, Hawksworth, Swindon, Wiltshire SN2 1TT.

Educational Supply Association (ask for Play Specials and Vital Years), School Materials Division, Pinnacles, Harlow, Essex.

Escor Toys Ltd., Groveley Road, Christchurch, Hampshire BH23 3RQ.

Fisher-Price Toys (Europe) Ltd., Lodge Farm Industrial Estate, Hopping Hill, Northampton NN5 7AW.

Four to Eight, Medway House, St Mary's Mills, Evelyn Drive, Leicester LE3 2BT.

Galt Educational Division, James Galt and Co Ltd., Brookfield Road, Cheadle, Cheshire SK8 2PN.

Huntercraft, ESA, PO Box 22, Harlow, Essex CN19 5AY.

Kiddicraft Ltd., Kenley, Surrey CR2 5TS.

London Music Shop, 154 Sidwell Street, Exeter EX4 6RT.

Playforms, Relyon, Hospitals Division, Wellington, Somerset.

Playskool, Milton Bradley Ltd., C. P. House, 97–107 Uxbridge Road, London W5 5TL.

Toy Aids Project (see above, under *Toys and Play Aids Suppliers*).

Toys for the Handicapped (suppliers of the Pethna range of equipment), 76 Barracks Road, Sandy Lane Industrial Estate, Stourport-on-Severn, Worcestershire DY13 9QB.

... But however much equipment the child has, the most valuable aid of all is an alert adult who can act as:

a toy

a climbing frame

an interpreter

a communicator

a comforter

a parent

a teacher and

a friend.

Afterword

'. . . there is a brightness within
my soul that words can never trace. I call it Life,
and laugh with its delight, though life itself be
out of sound and sight.'

Robert J. Smithdas, 1982
Director of Community Education,
Helen Keller National Center
for Deaf-Blind Youths and Adults,
New York.

Index